Weight Watchers New Complete Cookbook 2021

200+ Easy, Healthy and Delicious WW SmartPoints Recipes to Transform Your Body and Lose Weight

Lenore Morgan

Copyright © - All rights reserved.

Table of Contents

Chapter 5: Desserts 56

Chapter 6: Snacks 64

Conclusion 76

Introduction

Weight Watchers International Inc. is the most promising, effective, successful, and largest diet program specifically designed for weight loss. The company was initially formed by a woman named and has been growing globally for the past six decades. Smart Point is a numeric system that is based on counting in the Weight Watchers Program. It utilizes the principles of modern nutritional science and makes weight loss easier. It inclines you to have healthier and nutritious foods to ensure a sound, healthy, energetic lifestyle and of course weight loss. In this numeric system, every food is credited with a particular value which is based on four main things that include sugar, calories, protein, and saturated fat.

There are daily and weekly Smart Points so that you can track the amount of the food you are eating and what category of food you are eating. The Zero Points foods are having 0 Smart Point value and are selected because they are creating the basis for having a healthy and nutritious eating approach. They can also not be eaten in a bigger quantity than other foods. The WW Program is the best weight loss plan for sure.

Chapter 1: The principle of Weight Watchers

The principle of Weight Watchers is based on nutritional science and a program geared towards sustainable success. You are taught which foods and what food types are healthiest for you. This allows you to make healthier food decisions and no food is banned from the Weight Watchers program. This means it works alongside other diets and personal lifestyle choices. It also means that you don't feel limited or constricted in adopting this diet.

The goal is to lose weight through calorie reduction in a sustainable fashion through healthy eating. It also encourages the implementation of an exercise program and offers a local support group. You are invited to track your use and movements through activity tracker gadgets like the Fitbit. This will allow you to analyze what exercise you are doing and how it will work alongside your diet. The third principle is the support group where you will meet like-minded local people with this same aspiration has you.

You will also be guided by a success coach who has been on the same journey, has you? This is a vital part of Weight Watchers, and statistically, the more somebody attends the local meetings, the higher the likelihood of their success. It gives you the opportunity to tap into the wealth of knowledge available in the network and having a support group enhances your possibility of really succeeding long term.

Therefore, Weight Watchers operates on three key principles; healthy eating, a regular exercise program and a support group. There is also an online option where you don't attend meetings, but you have the opportunity to be part of an online community and network.

The program is very simple to follow and access to help readily available in the form of coaches, resources or the online or offline community. Firstly, you will have a confidential weigh in and set your ideal weight goal based upon your body mass index. If you are successful in this goal, you then begin a maintenance period for six weeks. This phase is to establish stability in your weight, and if successfully implemented you will become a lifetime member.

It's success factors are based upon a coach who has achieved success through the Weight Watchers program and a like-minded network which offers support, accountability, ideas and inspiration. This combined with the wealth of knowledge and tools online like the app, recipe ideas, expert chat facility, fitness videos and support network make you realize why it is the market leader in weight loss management.

Chapter 2: Food Cravings & How to Manage

That over-eating and food craving lead to weight gain, is a common knowledge. But, if you manage to overcome your food cravings, you can shed thousands of calories within no time. In this section, we explore the latest tricks by the researchers and experts as to how can you overcome your cravings.

Once you make up your mind to lose weight, you should try your best to avoid your triggers. For example, you crave for what you eat therefore, if you will switch to other things that you do not eat often, you will be able to weaken your old cravings. Studies say that this is the best way to eliminate your old cravings because the longer you avoid your trigger food, the lesser will be your craving for it. Ideally, you should switch to something healthy because in the end, you will possibly crave for the food items you have switched to. And, if you have switched to fresh fruits, it will be the real bonus.

Next trick is to destroy the temptation. If you have succumbed to a craving and bought your favorite junk food or any other trigger food and not feeling good while eating, destroy it. Do not throw it, but ruin it completely by running water over it. It will offer you the satisfaction that you have kicked your binge. However, you might feel bad that you have wasted money but just think if the junk food was not thrown away into the dustbin; it would have gone straight to your hips.

In order to eliminate your craving and clamp your appetite, drink two glasses of water and eat an ounce of nuts which includes walnuts, almonds, or peanuts. Within 20 minutes you will be able to overcome your craving completely. Moreover, nuts are quite good for your health, and if you eat them every day in an appropriate amount, you will definitely be amazed by the results.

Try switching to a skimmed latte, i.e. coffee, instead of going to your favorite restaurant and binging on unhealthy food. The caffeine it contains might not please your taste buds, but it can certainly save you the calories by satiating your craving.

Studies show that people in depression and stress tend to eat more. Therefore, it is important for you to learn how to deal with the stress. This way you will be able to shed lots of calories a day. However, this trick requires some practice. Deep breathing while relaxing or visualizing a tranquil scene on your own will be a good idea. You can divert to listening to powerful audios that teach progressive muscle relaxation.

When you are tired you feel like eating, therefore, it is the best time to take a power nap as it will reduce the exhaustion. The best thing you can do is shut the door, close your eyes and re-energize yourself.

After satisfactorily brushing your teeth in the morning, you wish not to eat anything for some time because you do not want to mess up the freshness. You can make the best use of this habit by brushing your teeth or by gargling with mouthwash. This is how you can control your food cravings, and you will definitely experience better results in the end.

Foods that are encouraged

The foods that are encouraged on the Weight Watchers plan are ones that are high in protein as well as those that have a lot of nutrients in them, such as fruits and vegetables.

Low-fat dairy is also encouraged for muscle health, and whole grains are a good thing to add to the meal to keep you full and healthy.

Eating lots of healthy produce is a good foundation to start with. These have all the nutrients that you need to stay healthy and happy while losing weight. They are low in calories but can really fill you up more than some of the other options, so having them as the base for most of your meals and snacks can really help to fight off the cravings and keep you full.

Protein is really encouraged on the new Smart Points system. You can choose many types of protein including fish, turkey, and chicken. Be careful with some of the other options, like hamburger, that are higher in saturated fats and will make your points go up.

And of course, having some whole grains is always good to keep healthy. These have a lot of the B vitamins that your body needs to stay healthy, and it will ensure that you are able to feel full for longer while eating fewer calories. Keep in mind that there are differences between the whole grains and the processed grains; the processed grains are basically just glorified sugars and will be treated as such when using this program.

These are the food items that are going to keep you the healthiest. They have the most nutrition inside and will fill you up while you are still eating fewer calories in the long run. They taste good, and there are quite a few options that you can make out of them to really enjoy the diet. Mixing in a bit of the discouraged items on occasion can really help to mix things up and keep you healthy.

Foods that are discouraged

While you are allowed to consume any kind of food that you want when on the Weight Watchers diet, the points are set up to discourage the eating of some kinds of foods. For example, you may be allowed to have cookies on occasion, but do you really want to use up all your points on just a few of them during the day and have nothing else to eat? Eating something that is discouraged on the plan is not going to completely ruin your progress, you just need to be careful how you use these and only have them on occasion.

There are a number of foods that are discouraged on the Weight Watchers plan. These are mostly foods that are high in sugar and saturated fats, but some that are high in processed carbs are going to be discouraged as well. Things like cookies, ice cream, fried foods, freezer food selections (ones that are in the freezer at the store, not the freezer meals you make for yourself at home), candy, cake, most baked goods, and more. If they are high in calories, they are probably high in points so keep this in mind when making a selection.

If you are uncertain about if a particular food is discouraged or not or you are curious about how many points it adds up to, make sure to check out the materials that you get from your meetings. This will help you to see how many points you would use up when it comes to eating that item that you want. Perhaps after seeing how many points that one item entails, you will decide that eating it is not worth all of that.

What about those drinks?

Another thing that you will need to consider when picking out what to eat during the day is what drinks you will be consuming. While options like green tea and water are not going to affect your points by much, there are some drinks that could take up as many of your points as a whole meal. These are mostly options like alcoholic and dessert drinks, and in reality, they are not giving you that many nutritional benefits for all the calories that are inside of them.

While you are allowed to have some of these drinks on occasion, you really need to watch the points and don't let them get away from you. Even regular fruit juices can be hard to fit within your points total because of all the sugar that is added to them and how Weight Watchers is discouraging items that have a lot of sugar.

If you don't want to ruin your points total for the day, it is best to stick with some simple options. Water and green tea are often the best because they contain few calories and won't take up all your points, but they provide the hydration that the body needs. Milk is a good option as well because it helps the body build strong bones and muscles. If you choose to have some juices, consider making some of your own so that you are able to avoid the extra sugars that are added to some of the store bought varieties.

How to pick your meals

You are going to get a lot of say in your meals. Not only are you allowed a certain amount of points each day, but you are also only going to get some extra points that are going to be used for any of the cheats or those days that you are going to be up and moving a lot. Outside of staying within the points, you are going to be able to make the right decisions for your needs.

The best idea is to plan out meals that are healthy and keep you healthy all day long. Foods that are full of healthy vitamins and minerals are going to be one of the best choices that you can make when trying to lose weight. If you are able to stick mostly with these healthier meals that have all the nutrition that you need, you are all set for doing well on this diet.

There are going to be times when you are going to eat out with friends, go to a party, or some other event that is going to mess with your plans a bit. Luckily, you are able to go through and make changes to the points that you eat through the day so that you have some points left over while still getting a lot of the nutrition that you need for good health. Plus, when you get to the party, you will realize how many points you have left and may find that it is easier to avoid overeating because you don't want to ruin all your progress.

And this is part of why so many people have seen success when they are on Weight Watchers. There are some rules that will help you out, but there is a lot of flexibility that you need to make sure that you are able to fit it into your daily life. With all the great choices that you will be able to make using your new point system, you will find that it is easier to get the good nutrition that you need while also losing weight and staying healthy.

At each of the meetings that you attend, you will be given some more information that will help you to make the right food choices for your needs. You get to pick which foods that you want to eat, but keep in mind that sticking mainly with the foods that are in the encouraged category will ensure that you are getting the right nutrition into the day and that you are able to eat fewer calories without feeling hungry and deprived on the diet. Eating some of the discouraged foods is not a bad thing on occasion, you just need to make sure that you are keeping them to a minimum as much as possible.

Chapter 3: Breakfast

WW Cheesy Quesadillas

Prepping Time: 15 minutes

Smart Points: 2

Servings: 1

Ingredients:

- 6 low-carb tortillas
- 30gms of leafy greens
- 2 eggs and 2 egg whites
- 170gms plain cream cheese
- 1-2teaspoons of ground psyllium husk powder

Toppings/Flavorings:

- 1 tablespoon coconut flour
- ½ teaspoon of salt
- Olive oil for frying the Quesadillas
- 150gms of grated cheese partly skimmed

Directions:

1. Start with preparing all the ingredients.

2. For the tortillas: Start by preheating the oven to 400 degrees F.

3. Beat the eggs and whites till fluffy then add the cream cheese and beat in a mixer for a smooth batter.

4. In a bowl, mix salt, the psyllium husk powder and coconut flour and keep adding spoonful of flour mixture into the egg batter and keep beating it.

5. Let the batter rest for a while. The batter should have a pancake batter-like consistency. If the batter is loose add psyllium powder to it.

6. Place parchment paper on 2 baking sheets and pour 3 circles on each sheet to get the 6 tortillas. The tortillas should be 5" in diameter and ¼" in thickness.

7. Bake for 5 minutes or until the edges turn brown.

8. For the quesadillas: Place a tortilla on a lightly greased skillet and add the greens, seasonings and cheese and cover it with another tortilla. Heat the skillet and cook till the cheese melts.

9. Cut the tortillas into wedges and serve with some salad greens and guacamole or hummus on the side.

10. Enjoy!

Avocado Breakfast Meal

Prepping Time: 5 minutes

Smart Points: 1

Servings: 1

Ingredients:

- 1 large avocado with the seed removed, cut in halves
- 1 tin of sardines that are drained
- 1 medium spring onion finely cut
- 1 tbsp. mayonnaise

Toppings/Flavorings:

- 1 tbsp. fresh lemon juice
- ¼ tsp. turmeric powder
- Salt

Directions:

1. Start with preparing all the ingredients them put the sardines in a bowl. Using a fork, break them into smaller pieces then keep aside.
2. Get the avocado and scoop the meat of the avocado and then set aside in a bowl. Try to leave around half to an inch of the avocado flesh.
3. In a bowl with the sardines, add finely sliced spring onions then mix. Stir in the mayonnaise, turmeric powder, and mix all the ingredients well.
4. Get the avocado meat and mash it until it reaches the desired consistency.
5. Add this mashed avocado to the bowl of sardines and spring onion mixture.
6. Squeeze some fresh lemon juice and add some salt.
7. Mix all the ingredients well.
8. Scoop this filling into each half of the avocado.
9. Serve and enjoy!

Spiced WW Cheese Recipe

Prepping Time: 15 minutes

Smart Points: 3

Servings: 2

Ingredients:

- 1 goat cheese log
- 1 pack mini buns
- 2 tbsp. olive oil
- 1/2 cup sun-dried tomatoes in oil, drained and chopped
- 1/2 cup fresh basil leaves

Spices:

- 1 tbsp. fresh flat-leaf thyme leaves
- 1 tbsp. fresh parsley leaves
- 1 tbsp. fresh tarragon leaves
- 1 tbsp. fresh mint leaves

Directions:

1. Start with preparing all the ingredients then combine the thyme leaves, parsley, tarragon leaves and mint leaves.

2. Roll cheese log evenly in herb mixture; wrap in plastic wrap. Chill for 24 hours or at least 2 hours before.

3. Prepare the oven by preheating to 350°.

4. Drizzle mini buns with olive oil then carefully press buns into muffin cups in muffin pans.

5. Bake for 9 minutes or until crisp and lightly browned.

6. Remove from oven and then let it cool for 5 minutes.

7. Top the goat cheese over the buns with sun-dried tomatoes and basil leaves.

8. Serve and enjoy!

Healthy Quiche Spinach

Prepping Time: 35 minutes

Smart Points: 1

Servings: 4

Ingredients:

- 8 organic eggs
- 225 grams Fresh spinach
- 150 grams Diced bacon
- 250 ml Heavy whipping cream
- 150 grams Shredded cheese

Toppings/Flavorings:

- 2 tbsp. Butter
- Salt and pepper

Directions:

1. Start with preparing all the ingredients then preheat your oven to a temperature of 350°F or 175°C.

2. Melt the butter in pan, once it heats up and melts, cook the bacon in butter till crispy.

3. After that, add the spinach.

4. In a bowl, beat the eggs then add the cream and whisk it further, till it mixes completely.

5. Get the beaten eggs and cream mixture and pour it into the greased baking tray.

6. Then add the fried bacon and spinach.

7. Top this up with the shredded cheese.
8. Place the dish in the middle of the oven and bake it for around 30 minutes
9. Serve and enjoy!

Breakfast Fish and Cheese

Prepping Time: 20 minutes

Smart Points: 3

Servings: 4

Ingredients:

- 2 pounds of salmon, single filet
- ½ cup Parmesan cheese, shredded
- 3 cloves of garlic, minced
- ¼ cup parsley, chopped
- Salt

Directions:

1. Start with preparing all the ingredients then prepare your oven by preheating to 425 degrees F. Set a baking sheet with parchment paper.
2. Season the salmon filet with salt then place the filet skin facing down on parchment paper. Cover with a second sheet of parchment paper and bake for about 10 minutes.
3. Mix the minced garlic, chopped parsley and parmesan cheese in a bowl then coat the salmon filet with the garlic mixture on top.
4. Return the salmon filet to oven and cook for another 5 minutes.
5. Serve and enjoy!

Classic Overnight Oats with Almond Butter

Prepping Time: 5 minutes

Smart Points: 2

Servings: 2

Ingredients:

- 3/4 cup old fashioned oatmeal
- 3/4 cup unsweetened almond milk
- 1 tbsp. chia seeds
- 1 tbsp. flaxseeds
- Coconut flakes

Toppings/Flavorings:

- Nuts
- Almond extract
- 1 tbsp. Almond butter

Directions:

1. Start with preparing all the ingredients then combine the oats, milk, chia seeds, flaxseeds, and almond extract in a mason jar.
2. Let the oatmeal stay in the fridge overnight.
3. Before eating or serving, add the almond butter and nuts.
4. Enjoy!

Scrambled Soy-bean and Spinach

Prepping Time: 10 minutes

Smart Points: 2

Servings: 2

Ingredients:

- 1 cup spinach
- 2 cloves garlic, minced
- 1 small red onion, diced
- 1 bell pepper, finely diced
- 170 g firm tofu

Flavorings:

- 1 tsp. turmeric
- Salt and pepper
- Olive oil

Directions:

1. Start with preparing all the ingredients then heat up a non-stick pan over medium heat then add olive oil and sauté the garlic, onion and red bell pepper for a few minutes until they start to soften.
2. Toss in the tofu and mash it with the spatula. Stir in the veggies, tofu, turmeric, salt and pepper and add a 3 tbsp. of water to the pan.
3. Continue stirring for about 5 minutes or until the tofu is starting to brown; add a bit of water when the pan is dry if the tofu is still cooking.
4. Serve and enjoy!

Sweet Cauliflower Florets Recipe

Prepping Time: 15 minutes

Smart Points: 1

Servings: 8

Ingredients:

- 1½ cups cauliflower florets
- ¾ cup coconut milk
- 1 tsp. un-sulphured blackstrap molasses

- 2 tbsp. pure maple syrup
- ½ tsp. cinnamon

Toppings/Flavorings:
- ⅛ Tsp. salt
- 1 tsp. pure vanilla extract
- 1-2 tbsp. cacao powder

Directions:

1. Start with preparing all the ingredients then start simmering the cauliflower florets and coconut milk in a small saucepan over medium heat. After some minutes, bring down the heat then simmer for another 5 minutes.

2. Using an immersion blender let the cauliflower and cream smooth until desired consistency.

3. Toss in all remaining ingredients and mix to combine. Transfer the mixture into a bowl.

4. Serve and enjoy!

WW Eggs Benedict

Prepping Time: 3 minutes

Smart Points: 4

Servings: 1

Ingredients:

For the sauce:
- 2 large organic egg yolks
- 2 tablespoons ghee, melted
- 1 tsp. freshly squeezed lemon juice
- Paprika, as you needed
- Cayenne pepper, as you needed

For the eggs benedict:
- 1 tsp. white vinegar
- 2 large free-range eggs
- ½ cup ready-made spiced pulled pork

Directions:

1. Start with preparing all the ingredients.

2. For the sauce: Start by using a microwave-safe bowl then gently whisk the egg yolks with the ghee, lemon juice, paprika, salt, and cayenne pepper.

3. Microwave the mixture for 20 seconds and then whisk again until the sauce is smooth then set aside.

4. To make the eggs benedict: Bring a small pot of water to a simmer then pour in the vinegar.

5. Crack the eggs into a small bowl, and roll them around lightly so that the whites surround the yolk of the egg.

6. Carefully pour the eggs into the simmering water and poach them for 3 minutes.

7. Meanwhile, put the heated pulled pork on a plate.

8. Remove the poached eggs from the water with a slotted spoon and dry them gently with a paper towel.

9. Place the eggs on top of the pulled pork and spoon the sauce over the eggs.

10. Serve and enjoy!

WW Eggs Muffins with Classic Sauce

Prepping Time: 15 minutes

Smart Points: 4

Servings: 4

Ingredients:
- 4 poached eggs
- 2 English Muffins cut in half
- 4 turkey bacon rashers
- 240 ml fat free Greek yogurt
- 3 egg yolks

Flavorings:
- ¼ tsp. Dijon mustard
- 1 tbsp. white wine vinegar
- Salt and pepper

Directions:

1. Start with preparing all the ingredients then start off with the hollandaise sauce by getting a small sauce pan then fill it with half of hot water then simmer.

2. Then get a bowl that can fit on top of the saucepan the beat the yogurt, vinegar and egg yolks together then mix well just make sure that the bowl will not touch the simmering water.

3. Continuously stir the mixture until thickened for about 12-15 minutes.

4. When thickened, remove from the heat and add in the salt, mustard and pepper and set aside.

5. Meanwhile, grill the turkey bacon and toast the English muffins.

6. In a pan of boiling water, poach the eggs and do not overdo them. The eggs should be slightly runny, not hardboiled.

7. On top of each toasted or grilled muffin, place a slice of bacon then place poached egg on the bacon. Garnish with hollandaise sauce and some pepper.

8. Serve and enjoy!

Vegan Green Flower Salad

Prepping Time: 8 minutes

Smart Points: 0

Servings: 4

Ingredients:

- 4 cups of broccoli florets
- 4 cups of cauliflower florets
- 2 tbsp. apple cider vinegar
- 4 tbsp. flaxseed oil
- 2 tbsp. scallions, chopped
- Toppings/Flavorings:
- 1 garlic clove, minced
- ½ tsp. dried mustard

Directions:

1. Start with preparing all the ingredients then steam the cauliflower and broccoli florets just until undercooked.

2. After that, transfer the steamed florets to a bowl and then let it cool.

3. Then in a small bowl, combine vinegar, oil, garlic, scallions, and mustard together.

4. Pour the dressing over the cauliflower and broccoli and then toss well to coat on the florets.

5. Serve and enjoy!

Chapter 4: Main Dishes

Delicious Ginger Kung Pao Chicken

Smart Points:3

Servings: 4

Ingredients:

- 1.33 lbs boneless skinless chicken breast, chopped
- 4 tsp sesame oil, divided
- 2 garlic cloves, minced
- 1 tsp. ginger, minced
- 2 celery ribs, chopped
- 1 red pepper, chopped
- 2 tbsp low sodium soy sauce (or coconut aminos)
- 1.5 tbsp sriracha (adjust to taste)
- 1 tbsp honey (adjust to taste)
- 1/2 tsp pepper
- 1/4 cup peanuts, chopped (use cashews for Paleo)
- 2 green onions, chopped

Directions:

1. Add half of the sesame oil to the pan. Add the chicken, garlic, and ginger. Cook for 5-7 minutes until just cooked through. Remove and set aside.

2. Add the remaining sesame oil to the pan. Add the celery and red pepper. Cook for 5-7 minutes until tender crisp.

3. Meanwhile stir together the soy sauce, Sriracha, honey, and pepper.

4. Add the chicken back to the pan and add the stir fry sauce and peanuts. Cook for 1-2 minutes so the sauce thickens. Remove from heat and let rest for 2-3 minutes so sauce can further thicken. Top with green onions.

Garlic Butternut Squash Turkey Skillet

Smart Points:3

Servings:4

Ingredients:

- 1 tbsp. olive oil
- 1 lb 99% lean ground turkey
- 2 garlic cloves, minced
- 1/2 onion, chopped
- 1 red pepper, diced

- 2 cups butternut squash, peeled and chopped
- 1 cup diced tomatoes (not drained)
- Salt and pepper
- 1 tsp. Italian seasoning
- 1/4 tsp. red pepper flakes
- 1 cup reduced fat feta cheese (or mozzarella)

Directions:

1. Heat the olive oil in a skillet over medium high heat. Add the turkey and cook, breaking up the meat, for 6-8 minutes. Add the garlic, onion, and red pepper. Cook for 4-5 minutes until onion begin to brown.

2. Add the butternut squash, tomatoes, salt, pepper, Italian seasoning, and red pepper flakes. Cover the skillet and cook until the butternut squash is tender, about 6-8 minutes. Add a touch of water or brown if anything begins to burn.

3. Add the cheese and cover for 1-2 minutes until it melts.

Delicious Pumpkin Porridge

Total Time: 20 minutes

Smart Points: 7

Servings: 2

Ingredients:

- 1/2 cup pumpkin puree
- 1 tbsp. brown sugar
- 3/4 cup quick oats
- 1 tsp. pumpkin pie spice
- 1/2 cup almond milk
- 1 1/4 cups water

Directions:

1. Add all ingredients into the instant pot and mix well.
2. Seal pot with lid and cook on high for 3 minutes.
3. Allow to release pressure naturally then open lid carefully.
4. Stir well and serve warm.

Fresh Green Beans and Tofu

Total Time: 25 minutes

Smart Points: 3

Servings: 4

Ingredients:

- 1 lb. green beans
- 1 small onion, chopped

- 2 tbsp. vegan butter
- 1 1/2 cup mushrooms, sliced
- 1/2 cup pureed tofu
- 1 cup vegetable broth

Directions:

1. Add butter in instant pot and select sauté once butter melted then add onion and mushroom and sauté for 3 minutes.
2. Add vegetable broth, green beans and pureed tofu. Stir well.
3. Seal pot with lid and cook for 15 minutes.
4. Release pressure using quick release method then open lid carefully.
5. Stir well and serve.

Asian Chicken Noodles with Broccoli

Prepping Time: 10 mins
Cook Time: 6 hours
Smart Points: 3
Servings: 6

Ingredients:

- 2 pounds of skinless and boneless chicken breasts
- 1 pound bag of broccoli florets
- ½ cup hoisin sauce
- 3 T rice vinegar
- 1 T minced ginger
- 1 chili pepper to use as a garnish, optional
- 6 oz., of soba noodles, left uncooked
- 3 minced garlic cloves
- 2 T cornstarch
- ¼ cup soy sauce
- 1 t sesame oil

Directions:

1. Mix the hoisin and soy sauces, garlic, cornstarch, ginger, and sesame oil with the water. Make sure it's combined
2. Add in chicken and then make sure the ingredients are coated. Cook for about 6 hours on low heat
3. About 30 minutes before it's done, cook the soba noodles, adding the broccoli in the last couple of minutes
4. Divide into bowls, shredding the chicken and adding the rice vinegar.
5. Put the chicken and sauce over the broccoli and soba noodles.
6. You can serve it with the diced chilles and chili pepper if you desire.

Garlic Chicken Marsala MeatBall

Smart Points: 5

Servings: 5

Ingredients:

- 8 ounces sliced cremini mushrooms, divided
- 1 pound 93% lean ground chicken
- 1/3 cup whole wheat seasoned or gluten-free bread crumbs
- 1/4 cup grated Pecorino cheese
- 1 large egg, beaten
- 3 garlic cloves, minced
- 2 tablespoons chopped fresh parsley, plus more for garnish
- 1 teaspoon Kosher salt
- Freshly ground black pepper
- 1/2 tablespoon all-purpose flour
- 1/2 tablespoon unsalted butter
- 1/4 cup finely chopped shallots
- 3 ounces sliced shiitake mushrooms
- 1/3 cup Marsala wine
- 3/4 cup reduced sodium chicken broth

Directions:

1. Preheat the oven to 400F.

2. Finely chop half of the Cremini mushrooms and transfer to a medium bowl with the ground chicken, breadcrumbs, Pecorino, egg, 1 clove of the minced garlic, parsley, 1 teaspoon kosher salt and black pepper, to taste.

3. Gently shape into 25 small meatballs, bake 15 to 18 minutes, until golden.

4. In a small bowl whisk the flour with the Marsala wine and broth.

5. Heat a large skillet on medium heat.

6. Add the butter, garlic and shallots and cook until soft and golden, about 2 minutes.

7. Add the mushrooms, season with 1/8 teaspoon salt and a pinch of black pepper, and cook, stirring occasionally, until golden, about 5 minutes.

8. Return the meatballs to the pot, pour the Marsala wine mixture over the meatballs, cover and cook 10 minutes.

9. Garnish with parsley.

Fast and Healthy Brussels sprouts

Total Time: 10 minutes

Smart Points: 4

Servings: 4

Ingredients:

- 1 lb. Brussels sprouts
- 4 tbsp. pine nuts
- 1 tbsp. olive oil
- 1/4 tsp. pepper
- 1/4 tsp. salt

Directions:

1. Place trivet on the bottom of instant pot then place steamer plate atop.
2. Pour 1 cup water into the pot.
3. Place Brussels sprouts on steamer plate.
4. Seal pot with lid and cook on high pressure for 3 minutes.
5. Release pressure using quick release method then open lid carefully.
6. Toss Brussels sprouts with olive oil, pine nuts, pepper and salt.
7. Serve and enjoy.

Apple and Butternut Squash Mash

Total Time: 20 minutes

Smart Points: 7

Servings: 4

Ingredients:

- 1 lb. butternut squash, cut into 2-inch pieces
- 2 apples, cored and sliced
- 1 cup water
- 2 tbsp. coconut oil
- 1 onion, sliced
- 1/4 tsp. cinnamon
- 1/8 tsp. ginger
- 1/4 tsp. salt

Directions:

1. Pour 1 cup water into the instant pot and place steamer basket inside the pot.
2. Toss apples, onion and butternut squash together and put in steamer basket. Sprinkle salt over the apple and butternut squash.
3. Seal pot with lid and select manual for 8 minutes. After 8 minutes release pressure using quick release method.
4. Open pot lid and transfer apple and squash mixture into the bowl. Using masher mash the apple and squash.
5. Add coconut oil, cinnamon and ginger in bowl and mix well until combined.
6. Serve warm and enjoy.

Healthy & Delicious Apple Crisp

Total Time: 15 minutes

Smart Points: 15

Servings: 4

Ingredients:

- 3/4 cup rolled oats
- 1/4 cup brown sugar
- 1/4 cup flour
- 4 tbsp. butter
- 1 tbsp. maple syrup
- 4 medium apples, peeled and chopped
- 1/2 tsp. salt
- 1/2 cup water
- 1/2 tsp. nutmeg
- 2 tsp. cinnamon

Directions:

1. Place chopped apples on the bottom of instant pot.
2. Sprinkle with nutmeg and cinnamon. Add maple syrup and water. Mix well.
3. Melt butter in bowl and mix together melted butter, brown sugar, salt, oats and flour. Add spoonful on top of apples mixture.
4. Seal instant pot with lid. Select manual high pressure for 8 minutes.
5. Use natural release method to open the instant pot.
6. Serve warm with vanilla ice-cream and enjoy.

Spinach Squash Risotto

Total Time: 15 minutes

Smart Points: 9

Servings: 4

Ingredients:

- 1 1/2 cups Arborio rice
- 3 cups fresh spinach, chopped
- 2 cups butternut squash, peeled and diced
- 1/4 tsp. oregano
- 1/2 tsp. coriander
- 8 oz. mushrooms, sliced
- 1/2 cup dry white wine
- 3 1/2 cups vegetable broth
- 1 bell pepper, diced

- 3 garlic cloves, minced
- 1 medium onion, chopped
- 1 tbsp. olive oil
- 1 tsp. pepper
- 1 tsp. salt
- 1/4 cup fresh parsley, chopped

Directions:
1. Heat olive oil in instant pot using sauté function.
2. Add squash, bell pepper, garlic and onion and sauté for 5 minutes.
3. Add rice in pot and stir well to combine.
4. Add oregano, coriander, pepper, mushrooms, dry wine, vegetable broth and salt. Stir well.
5. Seal pot with lid and cook on high pressure for 5 minutes.
6. Release pressure using quick release method then open lid carefully.
7. Add chopped parsley and spinach stir well and set aside for 5 minutes.
8. Serve warm and enjoy.

Instant Pot Garlic Chickpeas

Total Time: 45 minutes
Smart Points: 6
Servings: 4

Ingredients:
- 1 cup chickpeas
- 2 bay leaves
- 4 garlic cloves
- 4 cups water
- Salt

Directions:
1. Rinse chickpeas and place in instant pot.
2. Add bay leaves, salt, garlic and water in pot.
3. Seal pot with lid and select beans for 35 minutes.
4. After 35 minutes allow to release pressure naturally.
5. Open lid carefully and serve chickpeas with steamed rice.

Balsamic Glazed Pork Chop

Prepping Time: 10 mins
Cook Time: 6 hours
Smart Points: 8

Servings: 1 pork chop, 4 servings

Ingredients:

- 2 pounds of thick pork chopped, trimmed of fat
- 2 cups of green beans with the tough ends taken off
- 3 apples, cored and cut into wedges
- 2 heaping cups of chopped carrots
- 1 cup of fat free stock of choice

Marinade:

- 2 T balsamic vinegar
- ¼ t of dried rosemary and oregano
- ½ t dried thyme
- 1 T Dijon mustard
- ¼ cup low sodium soy sauce. You can also use coconut aminos
- 2 cloves of finely chopped garlic
- 2 T of honey
- 1 t ground black pepper

Directions:

1. Mix and put the chops in the marinade. Refrigerate it overnight
2. Put the pork chops in a pan and sear it on both sides, usually a couple of minutes on high heat until it's browned
3. Take it out of the pan and get any bits off the bottom with the marinade
4. Put the stock and veggies into the slow cooker, with the meat on top.
5. Cook it for about 4-6 hours, or until they're cooked and tender.
6. Serve immediately.

Avocado & Grape Salad with Walnuts

Prepping Time: 30mins

Cook Time: 45mins

Smart Points: 7

Servings: 4

Ingredients:

- 1 - avocado
- 2 - tablespoons freshly-squeezed lemon juice
- 1 ½ - cups halved grapes
- 1/3 - cup coarsely chopped walnuts
- ½ - cup sliced celery
- 1 - package baby arugula or baby kale
- 1 - green apple, cored, quartered

- ¼ - teaspoon kosher or sea salt
- ¼ - teaspoon black pepper

Directions:

1. Hurl avocado cuts in a single tablespoon lemon juice. Hurl apple cuts independently in outstanding tablespoon lemon juice.

2. Hurl grapes, walnuts, celery, apple, child kale or arugula, and salt and pepper together.

3. Cautiously include avocado and hurl.

4. Appreciate with a most loved clean eating plate of mixed greens dressing or vinaigrette served prepared in a plate of mixed greens or as an afterthought.

Scramble Eggs Veggie Avocado

Smart Points: 4

Servings: 4

Ingredients:

- 2 tsp. olive oil
- 2 cups broccoli, chopped
- 1 red pepper, chopped
- 1/2 cup onion, diced
- 8 eggs, whisked
- Salt and pepper
- 1 tomato, diced
- 1 avocado

Directions:

1. Heat the olive oil over medium high heat.

2. Add the veggies and cook for 3-4 minutes until tender crisp.

3. Add the eggs and stir frequently to scramble to desired doneness.

4. Top with salt, pepper, diced tomato, and avocado.

Smoked Ham & Apricot Dijon Glaze

Yield: 16

Smart Points: 5

Servings: 3 ounces

Ingredients:

- 1 (6 to 7 pound) Hickory smoked fully cooked spiral cut ham
- 5 tbsp. apricot preserves
- 2 tablespoons Dijon mustard

Directions:

1. Make the glaze: Whisk 4 tablespoons of preserves and mustard together.

2. Place the ham in a 6-quart or larger slow cooker, making sure you can put the lid on. You may have to turn the ham on its side if your ham is too large.

3. Brush the glaze over the ham. Cover and cook on the LOW setting for 4 to 5 hours. Brush the remaining tablespoon of preserves over the ham the 30 minutes.

Sweet Tea Glazed Pork Loin Roast

Prepping Time: 15 minutes

Cook Time: 1 hour

Smart Points: 6

Servings: 8

Ingredients:

- 2 pounds of pork loin roast

For the glaze, get the following:

- 4 cups water
- 8 bags of black tea
- Zest from two lemons
- 1 T olive oil
- 2 cups of blackberries, divided up
- ¼ cup tea reduction, keeping the reserve from the glaze
- 1 t cornstarch
- 1 cup sugar
- 6 sprigs of thyme
- 1 T olive oil
- ½ cup of diced onions
- ¼ cup chicken broth
- 2 T cider vinegar
- Salt and pepper for the taste

Directions:

1. For your glaze, you should heat the water and the sugar in a saucepan, boiling this and ten adding the tea bags, thyme, and the zest, letting it steep for about 30 or so minutes

2. Strain the mixture and then heat the tea over medium heat until you get a cup of this, usually about 30-35 minutes

3. Keep ¼ cup for the sweet tea sauce

4. While this is reducing, you should heat your cock pot and then baste the pork with the glaze every 10 minutes while the tea is cooking

5. Put it in the crock pot and heat it on high for at least an hour or two

6. Sauté the onion for about 3 minutes, until it is softened, then put the vinegar and cornstarch together, with the rest of the sauce until it's thickened

7. Break down the blackberries and then mix with the sauce

8. Take the pork out and let it sit, then put the blackberry sweet tea sauce on top of that before you serve this.

Parmesan Chicken Cutlets (Weight Watchers)

Prepping Time: 10mins

Cook Time: 25mins

Smart Points: 4

Servings: 3

Ingredients:

- ¼ - cup parmesan cheese
- 2 - tbsp dried seasoned Italian bread crumbs
- 1/8 - tsp paprika
- 1 - tsp dried parsley
- ½ - tsp garlic powder
- ¼ - tsp black pepper
- 4 - boneless chicken breast

Directions:

1. Preheat stove to 400 degrees.

2. In re-sealable plastic sack, consolidate cheddar, morsels and all seasonings; shake well.

3. Exchange blends to plate; dunk every chicken bosom in cheddar blend, swinging to coat all sides.

4. Organize on nonstick preparing sheet.

5. Prepare until chicken is cooked through, 20-25 minutes.

Cheesy Spaghetti & Turkey Sausage

Prepping Time: 15 mins

Cook Time: 2 hours

Smart Points: 8 with turkey sausage, 6 without

Servings: 8, about 1 ¼ cups

Ingredients:

- 1 pound of lean ground turkey sausage
- 1 jar of spaghetti sauce with no sugar
- 1 cup low-fat cottage cheese
- 1 cup low-fat ricotta cheese
- 1 T chopped fresh basil or a teaspoon of dried basil
- ½ t ground black pepper

- ½ pound of whole week spaghetti, uncooked and broken into small pieces before you add meat
- 1 cup shredded skim mozzarella cheese
- 1 t dried oregano
- Salt to taste

For the turkey sausage:
- 1 pound lean ground turkey or chicken
- ½ t ground black pepper
- 1 t dried oregano
- ½ t garlic powder
- 1 t dried sage
- ½ t cayenne pepper

Directions

1. Put the sausage ingredients and mix it together. Cook it on high and break the pieces until the turkey isn't pink anymore.

2. Take it off the heat and get rid of any fat, combining the meat with the marinara

3. Put the rest of the ingredients together with the turkey, and cook it on low for about 2 hours until the cheese bubbles.

4. You can also add in the spaghetti later, stirring it and then cooking for another hour if desired. If you don't' put in the spaghetti right away, you might have to cook it for another hour or so.

Kid-Friendly Baked Sweet and Sour Chicken

Prepping Time: 10mins
Cook Time: 20mins
Smart Points: 6
Servings: 8

Ingredients:
- 2 - pounds boneless skinless chicken breasts
- 1 - Tablespoon olive oil
- 2 - stalks green onion chopped
- ¼ - cup ketchup
- ¼ - cup honey
- 2 - Tablespoons reduce-sodium soy sauce
- 2 - teaspoons fresh ginger minced
- 1 - Tablespoon garlic minced
- 1 - teaspoon salt
- 1/3 - cup rice vinegar
- 2 - pouches Uncle Ben's Ready Rice whole grain

Directions:

1. Place the chook bosoms in a gallon-sized ziplock percent.
2. Add most of the people of the fixings to the ziplock % except for the rice wallet.
3. Close and blend to completely consolidate.
4. Place in the fridge and permit marinate so long as 1 day, or as meager as 30 minutes.
5. Preheat the broiler to 425 ranges.
6. When the broiler is preheated, upload the chicken bosoms to a shallow heating field.
7. Expel the cooked chook from the stove. Place on a slicing board and reduce into skinny cuts.
8. Microwave the 2 pockets of rice and serve quickly.

One Pot Beef and Cauliflower Mash

Prepping Time: 15 mins

Cook Time: 8 hours

Smart Points: 7

Servings: 6

Ingredients:

- 2 pounds of cubed beef stew meat
- 5 cloves minced garlic
- 1 cup beef broth
- 1 T smoked paprika
- 2 T light butter
- Salt and pepper for taste
- 1 chopped large onion
- 1 can diced tomatoes with roasted garlic
- 2 T Worcestershire sauce
- 1 head of cauliflower
- ¼ cup sour cream

Directions:

1. Mist a skillet with cooking spray and cook on medium high heat. Season your cubes and then brown them in the skillet well. Put them in the crock pot

2. Put the tomatoes, Worcestershire sauce, onions, broth, and garlic into there and mix it with the beef

3. Cook it for about 8-10 hours

4. Before it's ready to serve, about 15 mins, you should steam the cauliflower until it becomes tender.

5. Drain and put it in a bowl and then mash it with the butter and sour cream together. Season as desired

6. Serve your beef over the mash and with some mixed greens for best results.

Spicy Asian Chicken Meatballs

Prepping Time: 25mins

Cook Time: 45mins

Smart Points: 7

Servings: 18

Ingredients:

- 1 - pound (lean) ground chicken
- 1 - egg
- ½ - cup whole-wheat bread crumbs
- 1 - tablespoon Red Pepper powder or flakes
- ½ - cup green onions, finely diced
- 2 - teaspoons garlic powder
- 2 - teaspoons fresh
- ¾ - teaspoon kosher salt
- 3 - tablespoons honey
- 3 - tablespoons apple cider vinegar
- 3 - tablespoons tamari
- 1 - tablespoon sesame seeds
- 2 - tablespoons fresh cilantro

Directions:

1. Preheat stove to 350 degrees.
2. In a substantial bowl, combine ground chicken, egg, bread pieces, red pepper drops, green onions, garlic powder, ginger, and salt.
3. Put aside for 15 minutes to enable the breadcrumbs to grow, at that point fold into 1" balls.
4. Spot on a material lined heating sheet and prepare for 18-22 minutes, or just until the focal point of every meatball is cooked.
5. Exchange meatballs to an expansive skillet.
6. In a little bowl, whisk together nectar, vinegar, and tamari.
7. Spread skillet and swing stove to medium warmth, blending each 2-3 minutes as expected to shield the meatballs from adhering to the base of the container.
8. Cook just until the blend starts to steam.
9. Expel from warmth, sprinkle with sesame seeds and cilantro.
10. Serve meatballs promptly and appreciate

Delicious Chuck Roast Barbacoa

Prepping Time: 10 mins

Cook Time: 6-8 hours

Smart Points: 6

Servings: 10

Ingredients:

- 3 pounds of chuck roast, cut into chunks
- 1 can diced green chilles
- 6 cloves minced garlic
- 1 T cumin
- 2 t salt
- Juice from 3 different limes
- 1 diced onion
- 2-3 chopped chipotles in adobo sauce
- 2 T apple cider vinegar
- 1 T coriander
- 1 t black pepper
- ½ cup of fat free beef broth of choice

Directions:

1. Take all of your ingredients and put them into the slow cooker, mixing them.
2. Cook on low for 6-8 hours or until your meat can be shredded
3. Shred the meat and mix with the juices
4. Serve with a fork for best results

Skillet Lemon Chicken with Olives and Herbs

Prepping Time: 10mins

Cook Time: 10mins

Smart Points: 3

Servings: 4

Ingredients:

- ½ - tbsp extra virgin olive oil
- 8 - oz boneless chicken breasts
- ½ - tsp kosher salt
- 2 - teaspoons all purpose
- 2 - cloves garlic
- ½ - cup dry white wine
- ¼ - cup lemon juice
- 1 - teaspoon lemon zest

- 1 - teaspoon chopped fresh thyme
- 1 - cup pitted chopped olives
- 1 - tbsp chopped fresh parsley

Directions:

1. Preheat broiler to 400F with the rack in the inside position.
2. Warmth the oil in a 10-inch cast iron skillet over medium-high warmth.
3. Season chicken with salt and pepper at that point sprinkle with flour.
4. At the point when oil is hot, burn chicken around 3 minutes on each side.
5. Include garlic, wine, lemon pizzazz, lemon juice, thyme and olives.
6. Top with lemon cuts whenever wanted, exchange the skillet to the broiler and prepare around 10 minutes, until 165F in the inside.
7. Serve hot finished with parsley.

Seasoned Pinto Beans

Total Time: 25 minutes
Smart Points: 8
Servings: 4

Ingredients:

- 2 tbsp. olive oil
- 1 medium onion, chopped
- 1 lb. pinto beans, soaked overnight and rinsed
- 1/2 tsp. dried sage
- 1/2 tsp. dried oregano
- 1/2 tsp. garlic powder
- 1 can tomatoes, diced
- 4 cups water
- Pepper
- Salt

Directions:

1. Add 1 tbsp. olive oil in instant pot select sauté when oil heats up add onion and cook about 5 minutes.
2. Add soaked pinto beans, water and 1 tbsp. olive oil in instant pot and seal pot with lid then select bean/ chili mode.
3. When pot turns off then release the pressure using quick release method.
4. Now add tomatoes, sage, oregano, garlic powder, pepper and salt. Mix well until combined.
5. Select sauté mode on low set timer for 15 minutes to blend the flavors.
6. Serve warm and enjoy.

Crock Pot Chicken & Wedge Potatoes

Prepping Time: 15 mins

Cook Time: 6 hours

Smart Points: 5

Servings: 6

Ingredients:

- 2 pounds of boneless, skinless chicken breasts, cut into 6 different fillets
- 1 can of cream of chicken soup, a 10.75 oz., can
- 1 cup low-fat cheddar cheese, shredded up
- 1 t paprika
- 1 pound of gold potatoes, wedged up
- 1/3 cup fat-free chicken broth
- 1 T Worcestershire sauce
- Salt and pepper for taste

Directions:

1. Take the potatoes and put them into the slow cooker, seasoning them to taste
2. Season the chicken with the paprika, pepper, and the salt and put it over the potatoes
3. Whisk the soup and the broth together and put it over the chicken and the potatoes, cooking it on low for at least 6 hours
4. Transfer the chicken and potatoes to another plate and cover it with foil
5. Set the slow cooker to high heat and then put the Worcestershire and shredded cheese in there, mixing it, cooking for around 5 or so minutes until cheese melts.
6. Stir it until blended, and then put it over the chicken and the potatoes.

Slow Cooker Enchiladas

Prepping Time: 35mins

Cook Time: 45mins

Smart Points: 10

Servings: 6

Ingredients:

- 2 - large chicken breast filets with skin
- 16 - ounce jar red enchilada sauce
- 4 - ounce jalapenos
- ½ - teaspoon garlic powder
- 1 - teaspoon cumin
- 1 - teaspoon chili powder
- ½ - teaspoon black pepper
- 1 ½ - cups shredded cheddar cheese

- 8 - oz. container sour cream
- 6 - medium whole grain tortillas

Directions:

1. Preheat stove to 350 degrees. Place chicken bosoms in a secured preparing dish.

2. Prepare until juices run clear when pierced with a fork, after around 35-45 minutes. Evacuate skin and dispose of.

3. Shred chicken or cut into nibble estimated 3D shapes.

4. In a medium blending bowl include chicken, garlic powder, cumin, bean stew powder, dark pepper, and salt to taste.

5. Add to prepared chicken: green Chile peppers, 1/2 measure of enchilada sauce, 1/2 container acrid cream, and 1 glass cheddar.

6. Place 1/2 container chicken blend in the focal point of every tortilla.

7. Leave around 2" in the base without topping and overlay off.

8. Stack enchiladas in the moderate cooker; include a tad bit of the sauce over each layer as you stack them.

9. There ought to be 2 layers of 3 or 3 layers of 2, contingent upon the extent of your moderate cooker.

10. Consolidate the rest of the enchilada sauce and 1/2 container harsh cream. Pour over the enchiladas.

11. Pour fluid from moderate cooker over enchiladas and sprinkle with outstanding cheddar.

Roast Butternut Squash and Chickpea Salad

Prepping Time: 35mins
Cook Time: 45mins
Smart Points: 7
Servings: 4

Ingredients:
Salad:
- 1 - small 1 to 1-1/2 pound butternut squash
- 1- ¾ - cups cooked garbanzo beans
- 2 - cups spinach leaves
- Seeds from the butternut squash
- 1 - tablespoon olive oil or coconut oil
- ¼ - teaspoon salt
- ¼ - teaspoon pepper

Dressing
- 2 - tablespoons lime juice
- 2 - tablespoons soy sauce
- 1 - tablespoon virgin coconut oil

Directions:

1.   Preheat the broiler to 425 degrees. Line a sheet dish with material paper. Hurl squash with olive oil, salt, and pepper.

2.   One corner of the sheet dish, include seeds with olive oil, salt, and pepper.

3.   Seeds will be cooked following 5 to 10 minutes and can be expelled from the dish.

4.   Cook squash for 20 to 25 minutes, until squash pieces are fork delicate.

5.   Then, whisk together the dressing fixings.

6.   Delicately hurl squash with garbanzo beans, greens, and dressing. Spot on a platter or in a serving of mixed greens bowl.

7.   Top with toasted squash seeds and serve.

Chinese Chicken

Prepping Time: 45mins

Cook Time: 35mins

Smart Points: 14

Servings: 4

Ingredients:

Marinade:

- 1 - tablespoon peeled and minced ginger
- 1 - tablespoon garlic chili sauce
- 1 - tablespoon hoisin sauce
- 1 - tablespoon lite soy sauce

Chicken

- 1 - pound boneless, skinless chicken breasts
- 1- ½ - tablespoons canola oil

Instructions

1.   Whisk together the marinade. Put the chook portions in a bowl and hurl properly to coat equally with marinade.

2.   Cover and vicinity in the ice chest for around 20mins.

3.   Add canola oil to a sauté field over medium-excessive warm temperature. When the oil is warm and shining include the chicken pieces.

4.   Cook the fowl for three-five minutes until cooked via and the juices run clear. In the event that the bird pieces are larger, cook dinner longer.

5.   Serve over dark colored rice, darker rice noodles, or quinoa. Topping with cleaved cilantro or slashed scallions, whenever desired.

Slow Cooker Chicken Stew Recipe

Prepping Time: 15 mins

Cook Time: 6 hours

Smart Points: 3

Servings: 4

Ingredients:

- 4-6 boneless, skinless chicken thighs
- 1 cup fat-free chicken broth
- 1 chopped head of cauliflower
- 1 can of drained artichoke hearts
- 1/3 cup of Kalamata olives, drained
- 8 cloves of minced garlic
- 1 t salt
- 1 can of diced tomatoes
- ½ cup of plain, fat-free yogurt
- 1 sliced fennel bulb
- 1 sliced red onion
- ¼ cup chopped oregano
- 2 t lemon zest
- ½ t black pepper

Direction:

1. Spray a skillet with cooking spray and let it sit at medium high heat, browning the chicken on each side, typically taking about 5 minutes

2. Put the chicken into the slow cooker, putting the fennel, cauliflower, olives, and onion around the chicken.

3. Put the garlic, zest, salt and pepper, and the oregano over all of this

4. Put the broth and tomatoes into there

5. Cook it on high for about 4-5 hours or 6-8 on low

6. Put the yogurt and artichokes into there and then let it cook for about another 20-30 minutes, or until they're warmed and softened.

Chicken Cordon Bleu Soup

Prepping Time: 5 mins

Cook Time: 3 hours

Smart Points: 4

Servings: 4

Ingredients:

- 4 chicken breasts, boneless and skinless

- ½ cup fat-free milk
- 1 cup bread stuffing mix
- 1 can fat-free condensed cream of chicken soup
- 4 slices lean ham
- ½ cup blue cheese crumbles

Directions:
1. Take the chicken soup and milk and mix it, pour it into the slow cooker to cover bottom
2. Put the chickens over this
3. Cover it with the ham, and then ¼ cup of the bleu cheese crumbles
4. Cover and cook on low for at least 4-6 hours, 2-3 if you choose to use high heat

Slow Cook Beef Noodle & Mushroom

Prepping Time: 15 mins

Cook Time: 6-8 hours

Smart Points: 7

Servings: 4

Ingredients:
- ½ pound Portobello mushrooms
- 1 pound beef steak, cubed
- 2 T olive oil
- 2 cups beef broth
- 2 T cornstarch
- 2 cups cooked egg noodles
- 1 sliced onion
- ½ t salt
- ¼ cup red wine
- 1 T Worcestershire sauce
- ¼ cup cold water

Directions:
1. Put the onions and mushrooms into the slow cooker
2. Season the beef to taste with salt and pepper
3. Brown the beef on high in a skillet with oil
4. Put meat in slow cooker and use wine and about 1/3 of the broth that beef was in to deglaze it
5. Put the broth and the Worcestershire sauce together until mixed, adding it to the slow cooker
6. Cook on low for 6-8 hours or until meat becomes tender
7. Put the cornstarch and water together and then put it into the slow cooker for about 15-30 minutes, or until it's reached the right consistency

8. Cook the egg noodles, and then serve the beef tips with the mushroom gravy and the egg noodles for best results.

Delicious Turkey Kebabs

Smart Points: 0
Servings: 4

Ingredients:

- 1.33 lbs 93% lean ground turkey
- 1 egg
- 1/2 cup onion, minced
- 2 cloves garlic, minced
- 1/4 cup fresh parsley, chopped
- 1/2 tsp cumin
- 1/2 tsp garlic powder
- 1/2 tsp paprika
- 1/4 tsp coriander
- Salt and pepper

Directions:

1. Mix together all the ingredients until just combined. Try not to over mix to prevent the turkey from becoming tough.
2. Gently press the meat around wooden skewers to create kabobs. Refrigerate for 30 minutes. Alternatively, you can shape the meat into meatballs or logs and refrigerate for 30 minutes. Then gently thread them onto the kabobs.
3. Grill for 4-5 minutes per side or until turkey is cooked through.
4. To cook in the oven, broil for 4-5 minutes per side until cooked through.

Delicious Quick Red Cabbage

Total Time: 20 minutes
Smart Points: 3
Servings: 4

Ingredients:

- 6 cups red cabbage, chopped
- 1 tbsp. apple cider vinegar
- 1/2 cup applesauce
- 1 cup water
- 3 garlic cloves, minced
- 1 small onion, chopped
- 1 tbsp. olive oil
- Pepper

- Salt

Directions:

1. Add olive oil in instant pot and select sauté function.
2. Once oil heats up then add onion and garlic and sauté for 2 minutes.
3. Now add all remaining ingredients and mix well to combine.
4. Seal pot with lid and cook on high pressure for 10 minutes.
5. Release pressure using quick release method then open lid carefully.
6. Stir well and serve.

Bacon with Ranch Dressing Chicken

Prepping Time: 15 mins

Cook Time: 3.5 hours

Smart Points: 5

Servings: 4

Ingredients:

- 1 pound of boneless, skinless chicken breasts
- 3 cups plain, nonfat Greek yogurt at the temperature of your room
- 1 packet of ranch dressing mix, powdered
- 6 slices of turkey bacon, cooked and chopped up
- 1 cup fat-free chicken broth
- 1 T fresh chopped up chives or parsley

Directions:

1. Make sure that the Greek yogurt is at room temperature. After that, spray the crock pot with cooking spray and put the chicken breasts in there
2. Take a bowl and put all of the ingredients in there except for yogurt
3. Put the sauce on top of the chicken
4. Cook on high for about 3.5 hours
5. Put in the yogurt at room temperature and mix it, and then heat it for about 10 minutes or so until the sauce is warmed
6. Shred the chicken and then put the chives and parsley on top to garnish
7. You can serve it over miracle noodle pasta for no additional points

Fresh Vegetarian lasagna

Prepping Time: 20 mins

Cook Time: 2.4 hours

Smart Points: 5

Servings: 8

Ingredients:

- 1 package of whole wheat lasagna noodles, left uncooked
- 3 cups shredded reduced fat mozzarella
- 1 can diced tomatoes
- 3 Portobello mushroom caps, thinly sliced
- ½ cup liquid egg substitute
- ¼ cup fresh basil, chopped
- ½ t salt and pepper
- 1 container of fat-free ricotta
- 1 can of crushed tomatoes
- 1 can of chopped baby spinach
- 1 eggplant cut into quarters by length and sliced up thinly
- 5 cloves minced garlic
- 1 t dried oregano

Directions:

1. Put the egg substitute, ricotta cheese, the salt and pepper along with the oregano, and the veggies together into a bowl, mixing it

2. Mix the tomatoes and their juices, along with the basil and the garlic into a bowl

3. Put the cooking spray onto the slow cooker, and then put about a cup and a half of the tomato mixture into there, along with 5 egg noodles over this, overlapping slightly and breaking to cover

4. Then, put about half of the ricotta veggie mixture over the noodles and then pat it down firmly

5. Put 1/5 cups of the sauce on top of that and 1 cup of the mozzarella

6. Continue to do this, layering each time, with the noodles to start. You should top this with a third layer. Make sure to evenly spread the tomato sauce over the noodles, and put the last cup of mozzarella aside

7. Cook it on high for 2 hours or low for 4 hours

8. When done, put the rest of the mozzarella on top and then let it sit for about 10 minutes in order to melt the cheese.

Cheesy Chicken Green Bean Bake

Prepping Time: 40mins
Cook Time: 55mins
Smart Points: 10
Servings: 6

Ingredients:

- 1 - cup white instant rice
- ¼ - teaspoon black pepper
- ½ - teaspoon onion powder

- 1 - can cream of chicken
- 1 - cup cheddar cheese
- 1 - can of French style green beans
- 1 ½ - cups chicken broth
- Extra cheddar cheese for topping
- 3 - small chicken breasts

Directions:

1. Warmth broiler to 375°F/190°C.

2. In a goulash dish, join rice, pepper, and onion powder, cream of chicken, cheddar, green beans and chicken stock.

3. Blend until everything is consolidated.

4. Lay chicken over the rice blend. Space uniformly.

5. Cover with thwart and heat for 50 minutes.

6. Take off cover and best the chicken with more cheddar. Heat revealed for an additional 5 minutes or until cheddar is dissolved.

Sheetpan Italian Chicken and Veggie Dinner

Prepping Time: 40mins

Cook Time: 1hr 20mins

Smart Points: 8

Servings: 4

Ingredients:

For the Seasoning:

- 1 - teaspoon kosher salt
- ½ - teaspoon onion powder
- ½ - teaspoon dried oregano
- ½ - teaspoon dried basil
- ¼ - teaspoon thyme
- ½ - teaspoon sugar
- 1/8 - teaspoon black pepper
- 1 - clove crushed garlic
- 3 - tablespoons olive oil
- 2 - tablespoons red wine vinegar

For the sheet-pan:

- cooking spray
- 4 - oz each boneless skinless chicken thighs
- ½ - tsp kosher salt
- 12 - ounces zucchini

- 3 - carrots
- 1 - red bell pepper
- 1 - yellow bell pepper
- 1 - red onion
- chopped parsley for garnish

Directions:

1. Preheat stove to 450F stages. Shower 2 massive nonstick sheet skillets with oil or use cloth or thwart for simple cleanup.

2. Organize the middle rack and decrease third.

3. Join the Italian flavoring fixings in a widespread bowl. Season hen with half of teaspoon salt, at that factor include the bird, zucchini, carrots, ringer peppers and crimson onion to the bowl and hurl well to coat. Marinate 30 minutes or as long as medium-term.

4. Organize the whole lot onto the readied heating sheets spread out into solitary layer.The vegetables and fowl ought no longer touch.

5. Prepare round 20 minutes, turn hen and veggies and warmth an extra 10mins, till cooked and delicate. Top with crisp parsley and serve.

6. Cooler Friendly

7. Give the cooked dish a chance to cool totally.

8. Segment it into cooler holders and prevent for as long as 3 months.

9. To serve, defrost in the fridge medium-term.

10. Warm in a 325°F broiler till warmed via 20mins.

Southwestern Quinoa Salad

Prepping Time: 30mins
Cook Time: 1hr 25mins
Smart Points: 7
Servings: 8

Ingredients:

- Quinoa Salad
- 1 - cup uncooked quinoa
- 1 - ripe avocado
- 1 - cup thawed corn kernels
- 15 - ounce black beans, drained and rinsed
- 1- ½ - cups cherry tomatoes
- ¼ - cup coarsely chopped cilantro

Dressing:

- 2 - tablespoons extra-virgin olive oil
- 1 - tablespoon fresh squeezed lime juice
- 1 - teaspoon paprika

- 1/8 - teaspoon cayenne pepper
- ½ - teaspoon kosher or sea salt

Directions:

1. Bring 1/2 containers water and quinoa to a bubble. Decrease warmth to the most minimal setting and spread.
2. Permit to cook for 15 minutes or until all water is consumed. Turn off warmth and leave quinone spread on the burner for 5-10 minutes.
3. Cushion with a fork.
4. Chill quinoa in the cooler for no less than 1 hour or medium-term.
5. Prepare cooled quinoa with the rest of the plate of mixed greens fixings. Whisk together dressing fixings.
6. Add dressing to a plate of mixed greens and hurl to consolidate. Serve and appreciate

Mediterranean Tuna Salad

Prepping Time: 40mins

Cook Time: 35mins

Smart Points: 10

Servings: 2

Ingredients:

- 6 - ounce or jar of tuna
- ½ - cup artichoke hearts
- ½ - cup pitted kalamata olives
- 1 - roasted red pepper
- ¼ - cup fresh chopped parsley
- 2 - tablespoons slivered basil leaves
- 3 - tablespoons olive oil
- Juice of 1 lemon
- Salt and fresh ground pepper

Directions:

1. Merge most of the fixings in a bowl and season with salt and pepper.
2. Chill until sorted out to serve.
3. Serve in lettuce leaves, on a portion, or on total grain saltines.

Chicken slow cooker tacos

Prepping Time: 10 mins

Cook Time: 4-8 hours

Smart Points: 3

Servings: 4

Ingredients:

- 1 pound of the boneless, skinless chicken breasts
- ¼ t pepper and salt
- 2 t ground cumin
- ½ t chili powder
- 1 cup diced tomatoes
- ¼ cup chopped cilantro
- 4 taco shells
- Toppings you desire
- 1 T olive oil
- 1 t paprika
- ½ t onion powder
- ½ of a diced red onion
- 1 juiced lime
- 2 oz., of queso fresco, crumbled up

Directions

1. Season the chicken with some salt and pepper, letting it sauté in the olive oil and a skillet until it's browned on every side

2. Put the cumin, chili and onion powder, paprika, and the garlic in the crock pot with the chicken, covering it

3. Cook it on low for 6-8 hours until the chicken is tender

4. Towards the end, mix the onion, cilantro, and tomato in a bowl, seasoning with lime juice and some salt and pepper

5. Remove and shred with two forks, then serve the chicken in the shells, with the toppings of choice.

Sheet Pan Lemon Rosemary Chicken & Potatoes

Prepping Time: 25mins

Cook Time: 35mins

Smart Points: 6

Servings: 4

Ingredients:

- 3 - Tbsp olive oil
- 1 - Tbsp lemon juice
- Zest of 1 lemon
- 2 - cloves garlic
- 1 - Tbsp fresh rosemary
- 1 - Tbsp fresh thyme
- 1½ - tsp. sea salt

- 1 - tsp. black pepper
- 4 - boneless, skinless chicken breasts
- 3 - cups baby red potatoes
- 1 - lb. fresh green beans

Directions:

1. Preheat stove to 400 degrees F.

2. In a little bowl, whisk together 2 tablespoons olive oil, lemon juice, get-up-and-go, garlic, rosemary, thyme, salt and pepper.

3. In a different bowl hurl together potatoes with tablespoon olive oil and season with extra salt and pepper, whenever wanted.

4. On an extensive heating sheet softly splashed with oil, orchestrate chicken bosoms, potatoes and green beans and sprinkle herb blend over best, utilizing a brush or your hands to ensure everything is equally covered.

5. Place the skillet in the broiler and dish for 25 to 30 minutes, contingent upon the measure of your bosoms.

6. Chicken ought to have an inward temp of 165 degrees F, potatoes ought to be delicate and green beans decent and fresh.

7. Don't hesitate to turn the grill on for two or three minutes in the event that you like your potatoes fresher.

8. Serve and appreciate

6-Ingredient Mexican-Style Quinoa Salad

Prepping Time: 15mins
Cook Time: 25mins
Smart Points: 5
Servings: 4

Ingredients:

- ½ - cup dry quinoa, pre-rinsed
- 15 - ounce black beans
- 1 - cups salsa, no-sugar added
- 1 - cup corn kernels
- 1 - teaspoon chili powder
- 1 - avocado

Directions:

1. Include 1 container water and quinoa to a medium pot and convey to a moving bubble over medium-high warmth.

2. Diminish warmth to a stew, spread and cook until most dampness is assimilated around 12-15 minutes.

3. Turn off warmth and leave secured quinoa on the burner for 5 minutes.

4. Add to cooked quinoa, dark beans, salsa, corn, and stew powder. Add salt and pepper to taste.

5. Hurl to consolidate at that point include diced avocado and delicately hurl.

6. Add a plate of mixed greens to a serving dish and serve.

7. A plate of mixed greens can likewise be delighted in the virus.

8. Appreciate

Sheet Pan Chicken Fajitas

Prepping Time: 15mins
Cook Time: 20mins
Smart Points: 16
Servings: 4

Ingredients:

- 1 - lb. boneless, skinless chicken breasts
- 1 - red bell pepper
- 1 - yellow bell pepper
- 1 - poblano pepper
- 2 - jalapenos
- 1 - large or 2 small onions
- 2 - tablespoons taco seasoning
- 2 - tablespoons olive oil
- 8-10 - flour tortillas

Directions:

1. Preheat stove to 425 degrees. Shower or brush substantial 13x18 sheet dish with oil.

2. Cut chicken bosoms contrary to what would be expected into 1/4" to 1/2" wide strips.

3. Cut chime and poblano peppers into long thin cuts, approx. 1/4" wide.

4. Cut stem end from jalapenos. Utilize vegetable peeler to remove layer and seeds.

5. Cut finishes off of onions. Cut down the middle from shaft to post. Cut into thin cuts.

6. Disperse peppers, onions, and chicken on sheet container.

7. Sprinkle on taco flavoring. Shower with olive oil. Use tongs to hurl until everything is covered and spread in an even layer.

8. Prepare revealed for 30 minutes, mixing part of the way through.

9. Envelop tortillas by thwart and put in stove with fajita blend amid most recent 10 minutes of preparing time.

10. Embellishment sheet skillet with cilantro sprigs and lime wedges. Present with warm tortillas and discretionary fixings.

Lasagna with Fresh Tomatoes and Zucchini

Prepping Time: 1hr 10mins

Cook Time: 45mins

Smart Points: 7

Servings: 6

Ingredients:

- 10 - whole wheat or fortified
- 4 - ounces fresh or good quality part-skim or lower-fat mozzarella,
- 1 - cup skim or low-fat ricotta cheese
- ½ - cup finely grated Parmesan cheese
- 3 - cups coarsely chopped tomatoes
- ½ - teaspoon salt
- 2 - cloves garlic, minced
- 2 - tablespoons extra virgin olive oil
- 1 - medium yellow or green zucchini
- ½ - tablespoon Italian seasoning

Directions:

1. Preheat the broiler to 375 degrees F.

2. In a little bowl, combine ricotta, squash, 1/4 measure of the Parmesan, and half of the mozzarella.

3. Puree the tomatoes, salt, garlic, Italian flavoring or crisp herbs, and 1 tablespoon of the olive oil in a blender or nourishment processor on high until smooth.

4. Shower or coat the bottoms and sides of the ramekins or preparing dishes with olive oil.

5. Include a spoonful of tomato sauce to the base of each.

6. Tear or cut the lasagna noodles into 4 pieces. Spot one bit of lasagna noodle, top with ricotta blend, top with a noodle, include sauce and mozzarella, and after that include the ricotta blend, and rehash.

7. For the last layer of each, top the majority of the ramekins with a lasagna noodle, a portion of the tomato sauce, at that point a cut of the tomato and a sprinkle of the Parmesan cheddar and some crisply ground dark pepper.

8. Spread every ramekin firmly with foil and heat for 25 minutes. Evacuate the foil and prepare for an extra 5 minutes.

Balsamic Chicken

Prepping Time: 10mins

Cook Time: 10mins

Smart Points: 16

Servings: 4

Ingredients:

- 2 - tsp vegetable oil
- 3 – Tbs. balsamic vinegar
- 2 - tsp Dijon mustard
- 1 - cloves garlic
- 1 - pound uncooked boneless, skinless chicken breasts
- 2 - cups fresh mushrooms
- 1/3 - cup canned chicken broth
- ¼ - tsp dried thyme

Directions:

1. In a nonstick skillet, warm 1 teaspoon of oil.
2. In a medium bowl, blend 2 tablespoons of vinegar, the mustard and garlic.
3. Exchange chicken and marinade to skillet. Sauté chicken until cooked through, around 3 minutes on each side.
4. Include 4 basil leaves and cook for 1 minute. Exchange chicken to a platter and keep warm.
5. Warmth remaining teaspoon of oil in skillet. Sauté mushrooms for 1 minute. Include juices, thyme and remaining tablespoon of vinegar.
6. Cook, blending once in a while, until mushrooms are a profound dark colored shading, around 2 minutes
7. Serve chicken finished with mushrooms and cleaved basil leaf

Weight Watchers Breaded Chicken Cutlets

Prepping Time: 15mins
Cook Time: 25mins
Smart Points: 5
Servings: 4

Ingredients:

- ¼ - cup parmesan cheese, grated
- 2 - tablespoons dried Italian seasoned breadcrumbs
- 1/8 - teaspoon paprika
- 1 - teaspoon dried parsley
- ½ - teaspoon garlic powder
- ¼ - teaspoon fresh ground pepper
- 4 - boneless skinless chicken breasts, about 1 pound

Directions:

1. Preheat stove to 400°F.
2. In a re-sealable plastic sack, join cheddar, pieces and all seasonings; shake well.

3. Exchange blends to plate; dunk every chicken bosom in cheddar blend, swinging to coat all sides.

4. Orchestrate on a nonstick heating sheet.

5. Prepare until chicken is cooked through, 20 to 25 minutes.

Weight Watchers Egg Roll in a Bowl

Prepping Time: 10mins

Cook Time: 15mins

Smart Points: 6

Servings: 4

Ingredients:

- 1 - tsp minced ginger
- 4 ½ - cups packaged coleslaw mix
- ½ -cups shredded carrots
- 3 - medium cooked scallions
- 3 - Tbsp low sodium soy sauce
- 1 ½ - tsp sesame oil
- 1 ½ - tsp sugar
- 1 - pound uncooked ground chicken breast

Directions:

1. Dark colored the hotdog/meat in a medium nonstick skillet until cooked right through and afterward include the ginger.

2. Include soy sauce, sugar, and sesame oil.

3. Include full pack of coleslaw, mix till covered with sauce

4. Include 1/2 pack of destroyed carrots, still till covered with sauce

5. Include slashed scallions, blend altogether and cook on medium high warmth until the Cole slaw has decreased considerably.

Creamy Fennel Salad, Orange Wedge, Fresh Mint

Prepping Time: 1hr 25mins

Cook Time: 55mins

Smart Points: 6

Servings: 4

Ingredients:

- 3 - medium-sized fennel bulbs
- 1 - lemon
- ¼ - cup olive oil
- 1 - tablespoon Dijon mustard

- 1 - teaspoon salt
- ½ - cup fresh mint leaves
- ¼ - cup chopped fennel fronds
- 1 - orange
- Freshly ground black pepper

Directions:

1. Clean the fennel with the resource of washing the outside of the knob.
2. Shave the fennel with a mandolin or with a blade by using reducing carefully over the surface.
3. The fennel ought to be cut slim.
4. Hurl in a bowl with the mint, the ¼ diploma of the slashed fennel fronds and orange wedges.
5. Dressing Directions:
6. In a bit bowl positioned the Dijon mustard and overwhelm in the juice of one lemon.
7. Gradually shower in the olive oil, rushing as you move.
8. Add salt to flavor, and maintain on racing till absolutely consolidated and velvety.
9. Sprinkle dressing over the plate of combined veggies and hurl to consolidate.
10. Sprinkle with newly ground dark pepper to flavor.

Slow Cooker Chicken Pot Roast

Prepping Time: 1hr 5mins
Cook Time: 2hrs 20mins
Smart Points: 12
Servings: 6

Ingredients:

- 1 - large roasting chicken
- 2 - teaspoons extra-virgin olive oil
- 2 - garlic cloves
- 2 - teaspoons fresh thyme
- 1 - teaspoon black pepper
- 1 - teaspoon paprika
- 1 - teaspoon kosher
- 2 - stalks celery
- ¼ - cup water
- 1 - cup baby carrots
- 2 - medium potatoes

Directions:

1. Wash and pat dry hen. Rub the outside of chook with olive oil. Join flavors and rub outwardly of the fowl.

2. Place minced garlic within the pit along rather greater salt and pepper.

3. Add water to the slight cooker, subsequent the celery and the fowl to complete the whole lot, bosom facet up.

4. The celery keeps the chicken from caramelizing lots on the base.

5. Include carrots and potatoes around chicken.

6. Utilize a meat thermometer to check for doneness or pierce with a fork, to ensure the juices run clear.

7. For additional caramelizing, cautiously expel chook from the moderate cooker, installed a big simmering skillet and sear until desired shading has been come to. Trimming hen with new thyme, each time desired.

Supermodel Superfood Salad

Prepping Time: 15mins
Cook Time: 35mins
Smart Points: 6
Servings: 6

Ingredients:
* One head of kale
* ¼ - cup pine nuts
* ½ - cup dried cranberries or currants
* Juice of 1 lemon
* ¼ - cup extra-virgin olive oil
* Pinch of kosher

Directions:
1. Evacuate and dispose of substantial stems of kale leaves.
2. Coarsely hack kale leaves and add to an extensive serving bowl.
3. Include pine nuts, dried cranberries or currants.
4. Crush the juice of one lemon, shower with olive oil, and sprinkle salt, hurl to consolidate.
5. Whenever wanted, decorate with 1/4 container newly ground parmesan cheddar.

One-Skillet Chicken and Broccoli Dinner

Prepping Time: 35mins
Cook Time: 15mins
Smart Points: 10
Servings: 6

Ingredients:
* 1 - tablespoon extra-virgin olive oil
* 4-6 - ounce boneless, skinless chicken breasts

- 2 - cups broccoli florets
- 2 - cloves garlic
- ½ - cup chopped yellow onion
- ½ - cup sliced celery
- ¼ - cup chicken broth
- ¼ - teaspoon kosher
- ¼ - teaspoon black pepper

Sauce:
- ¼ - cup Coconut amino
- 2 - tablespoons vegetable Sriracha

Directions:

1. Evacuate the fowl and positioned aside.

2. Include broccoli florets and delicately sauté till marginally delicate.

3. Add the onion and celery to the skillet and prepare dinner for 5 to eight minutes, until the celery has diminished, and the onion is translucent.

4. Include the garlic and cook dinner for 30 seconds, until aromatic.

5. Include the juices, hen, and broccoli lower back to the skillet alongside the salt and pepper.

6. Cook elements for around 5mins, till chicken is warmed through.

7. For sauce, whisk collectively fixings and upload to the chance a minute in the past of cooking time.

Kale and Roasted Yam Salad

Prepping Time: 30mins

Cook Time: 35mins

Smart Points: 7

Servings: 4

Ingredients:
- 1 - bunch lacinato
- 1 - sweet potato
- 1 - tablespoon extra-virgin olive oil
- 1 - ripe avocado, peeled, pitted and cut into slices
- 2 - teaspoons freshly squeezed lemon
- 1 - tablespoon sesame seeds
- 1/3 - cup pumpkin or shelled sunflower seeds
- 1 - cup (half pint) cherry or grape tomatoes
- ½ - teaspoon kosher or sea salt
- ¼ - teaspoon black pepper

Directions:

1. Preheat broiler to 375 degrees. Hurl sweet potatoes in olive oil, 1/4 teaspoon of the salt, and 1/8 teaspoon pepper.

2. Spread on a material lined or nonstick heating sheet.

3. Cook for 25 minutes, flipping the pieces part of the way through, or until fork delicate and caramelized a bit.

4. Include kale, tomatoes, sweet potatoes, remaining 1/4 teaspoon salt, and 1/8 teaspoon dark pepper to a serving of mixed greens bowl and hurl.

5. Sweet potato pieces might be included warm or cool. Sprinkle the plate of mixed greens with sesame seeds and pumpkin seeds or sunflower seeds.

6. Tenderly prepare avocado cuts in lemon/lime squeeze, and extra best of the plate of mixed greens.

7. Appreciate with your most loved dressing or straightforward vinaigrette.

Sesame Chicken (Weight Watchers)

Prepping Time: 20mins

Cook Time: 11mins

Smart Points: 5

Servings: 4

Ingredients:

- 2 - tbsp sesame seeds
- 1 - tbsp water
- 1 - tbsp low-sodium soy sauce
- 1 - tbsp maple syrup
- 1 - tbsp dry sherry
- 1 - tsp fresh ginger root
- ½ - tsp five-spice powder spices
- 2 - tbsp all-purpose flour
- ½ - tsp salt
- ¼ - tsp black pepper
- 1 - lb uncooked boneless skinless boneless, skinless chicken breast
- 2 - tsp peanut oil

Directions:

1. Place an expansive nonstick skillet over medium-high warmth.

2. Include sesame seeds and cook until softly toasted, shaking container much of the time, around 2 to 3 minutes; exchange seeds to a shallow dish and put aside.

3. Whisk water, soy sauce, maple syrup, sherry, ginger and five-flavor powder together in a little bowl; put aside.

4. Consolidate flour, salt and pepper together in a shallow dish; add chicken and swing to coat.

5. Shake chicken pieces to evacuate abundance flour.

6. Warmth oil in a huge nonstick skillet over medium-high warmth. Include chicken and sauté until caramelized on all sides, around 5 minutes.

7. Add soy sauce blend to chicken and cook until sauce thickens and is nearly vanished, around 2 to 3 minutes more.

8. Plunge chicken pieces in toasted sesame seeds and serve, sprinkled with any extra soy sauce blend.

Fresh & Hearty Salad

Prepping Time: 20mins

Cook Time: 25mins

Smart Points: 5

Servings: 4

Ingredients:

- 6 - containers child blended plate of mixed greens
- 1 - green chile pepper
- 1 - container jolted
- 1 - container split cherry tomatoes
- ¼ - container cut almonds
- ½ - container defrosted
- 1 - tablespoon additional virgin olive oil
- ½ - teaspoon dried oregano
- ½ - teaspoon Dijon mustard
- ¼ - teaspoon legitimate
- ¼ - teaspoon dark pepper

Directions:

1. Whisk together oregano, red wine vinegar, Dijon mustard, salt, and pepper.

2. Gradually shower in olive oil, whisking while at the same time pouring.

3. Prepare all serving of mixed greens fixings together in a huge plate of mixed greens bowl.

4. Include plate of mixed greens dressing and hurl or serve as an afterthought.

5. Appreciate

Chapter 5: Desserts

Coconut Cranberry Crack Bars

Prepping Time: 10 minutes

Cook Time: 0 minutes

Smart Points: 4

Servings: 20

Ingredients:

- 1/2 cup organic cranberries, unsweetened
- 2 1/2 cups shredded coconut flakes, unsweetened
- 1/4 cup monk fruit sweetener syrup
- 1 cup coconut oil, melted

Directions:

1. Place berries and coconut in a blender and pulse for 1 minute until thick mixture comes together that resembles crumbs.
2. Tip the mixture in a bowl, add remaining ingredients and stir until well combined.
3. Spoon this mixture into a square baking tray, about 8 by 8 inch, and then press the mixture firmly using wet hands.
4. Place the baking tray into the freezer for 15 minutes or until firm.
5. Then take it out and cut into square bars.
6. Serve straightaway.

Vanilla Custard

Prepping Time: 5 minutes

Cook Time: 5 minutes

Smart Points: 2

Servings: 4

Ingredients:

- 1 teaspoon erythritol
- 1 teaspoon vanilla extract, unsweetened
- ¼ cup melted coconut oil
- 6 egg yolks, pastured
- ½ cup almond milk, full-fat and unsweetened

Directions:

1. Place egg yolks in a medium-sized heatproof bowl, add erythritol, vanilla, and almond milk and whisk together these ingredients using a stick blender until smooth.
2. Then slowly whisk in coconut oil until incorporated.

3. Place a saucepan, half full with water, over a medium heat and bring to simmer.

4. Place the bowl containing egg mixture over simmering water, insert a food thermometer into the mixture and cook for 3 minutes or until thickened and food thermometer reads 140 degrees F, whisking continuously.

5. Then carefully remove the bowl from the water bath and let custard chilled into the refrigerator.

6. Serve straightaway.

Hot Chocolate Ice Cream

Prepping Time: 10 minutes

Cook Time: 0 minutes

Smart Points: 4

Servings: 12

Ingredients:

- 2 tablespoons organic cocoa powder, unsweetened
- 4 scoops chocolate protein powder
- 2 tablespoons monk fruit sweetener
- 28-ounce chilled coconut milk, full-fat and unsweetened

Directions:

1. Place a loaf pan into the freezer and let chill.

2. In the meantime, separate coconut milk and cream and place cream in a bowl.

3. Whisk using an electric stand mixer until smooth, then whisk in coconut milk until blended.

4. Add remaining ingredients and whisk until just mixed, don't over-mix.

5. Spoon the mixture into the chilled loaf pan and return pan into the freezer until ice cream is set, stirring ice-cream every 20 minutes in the first hour.

6. When ready to serve, take out the loaf pan, let rest at room temperature for 15 minutes and then scoop out ice cream using a wet ice cream scoop.

7. Serve immediately.

Cranberry Sauce

Prepping Time: 5 minutes

Cook Time: 5 minutes

Smart Points: 3

Servings: 10

Ingredients:

- 3 cups unsalted almonds
- 1/8 teaspoon sea salt
- 1/8 teaspoon cinnamon

- 1 cup monk fruit sweetener, granulated
- 1 teaspoon vanilla extract, unsweetened
- 1/4 cup filtered water

Directions:

1. Place a large skillet pan over medium heat and when hot, add salt, cinnamon, sweetener, vanilla, and water.

2. Stir until well combined and cook until sweetener is melted completely and begin to crystallize, stirring frequently.

3. Then remove the pan from the heat and let the mixture sit at room temperature for 2 minutes.

4. Add almonds to the mixture and stir immediately using a wooden and then spread the mixture evenly on a lined baking sheet in a single layer.

5. Let almonds rest to cool completely for 10 to 15 minutes.

6. Then break the almonds properly and serve.

Chocolate Pudding

Prepping Time: 5 minutes

Cook Time: 1 minute and 30 second

Smart Points: 3

Servings: 2

Ingredients:

- 2 tablespoons erythritol
- 1 tablespoon organic cocoa powder, unsweetened
- 1/2 teaspoon glucomannan powder
- 1 cup coconut milk, full-fat and unsweetened

Directions:

1. Pour milk in a heatproof bowl and whisk in erythritol and cocoa powder until well combined.

2. Then slowly whisk in glucomannan powder and then microwave the mixture for 1 minute and 30 seconds at high heat setting or until hot.

3. Then remove bowl from microwave, whisk the pudding and cover bowl with the lid.

4. Place the bowl in the refrigerator until pudding is chilled and thick.

5. Serve when ready.

Peanut Butter Fudge

Prepping Time: 5 minutes

Cook Time: 1 minute

Smart Points: 3

Servings: 12

Ingredients:
- 1/2 cup peanut butter
- 1/2 cup cocoaut oil
- 2 tablespoons erythritol sweetener
- Melted chocolate for serving

Directions:

1. Place butter and oil in a heatproof bowl and microwave for 1 minute or more until butter and oil melt together, stirring halfway through.

2. Then stir in sweetener until well combined.

3. Take a 12 cups muffin tray, line each cup with a muffin liner and evenly pour in prepare fudge mixture.

4. Place muffin tray into the freezer and chill until hard.

5. When ready to serve, take out fudge from muffin cups, drizzle with melted chocolate and serve.

aramel Sauce

Prepping Time: 5 minutes

Cook Time: 15 minutes

Smart Points: 3

Servings: 12

Ingredients:
- 3 tablespoons monk fruit sweetener
- 1/3 cup salted butter
- 1 teaspoon vanilla extract, unsweetened
- 2/3 cup heavy cream, full-fat

Directions:

1. Place a medium saucepan over low heat, add butter and sweetener, stir until mixed and let heat for 4 to 5 minutes or until butter melt completely and golden brown, stirring frequently.

2. Then turn heat to medium-low, stir in cream and bring the mixture to boil.

3. Reduce heat to low heat and simmer sauce for 7 to 10 minutes or until thick enough to coat the back of a spoon.

4. Then remove the pan from heat, stir vanilla into the sauce and let cool slightly.

5. Drizzle sauce over sliced fruits and serve.

Cappuccino Cheesecake Mousse

Prepping Time: 15 minutes

Cook Time: 0 minutes

Smart Points: 3

Servings: 8

Ingredients:

- 1/4 cup coffee, unsweetened and strongly brewed
- 2 teaspoons vanilla stevia
- 16 ounces full-fat cream cheese, softened
- 1 cup heavy whipping cream, full-fat
- 1/2 cup almond milk, full-fat and unsweetened

Directions:

1. Pour coffee into a bowl, add cream cheese and whisk using an electric stand mixer at high speed until smooth.
2. Pour in milk and ½ teaspoon of stevia and whisk again until well combined and smooth.
3. Then blend in cream at high speed for 5 to 7 minutes or until mixture thickens.
4. Pipe this mixture into serving glasses and place in refrigerator for 10 minutes or until chilled.
5. Serve straight away.

Chocolate and Hazelnut Spread

Prepping Time: 10 minutes

Cook Time: 2 minutes

Smart Points: 3

Servings: 6

Ingredients:

- 5-ounce hazelnuts
- 2 tablespoons organic cocoa powder, unsweetened
- 1 teaspoon vanilla extract, unsweetened
- ¼ cup coconut oil
- 1-ounce unsalted butter

Directions:

1. Place a frying pan over medium heat and when hot, add hazelnuts and cook for 1 to 2 minutes or until nicely golden brown and roasted.
2. When roasted, remove the pan from heat and let nuts cool for 5 minutes.
3. Then remove the shell from the nuts by rubbing them with a kitchen towel.
4. Place nuts into a food processor along with remaining ingredients and pulse for 1 to 2 minutes at high speed or until smooth.
5. Tip the spread in a bowl and serve.

Peppermint Patties

Prepping Time: 10 minutes

Cook Time: 2 minutes

Smart Points: 3

Servings: 24

Ingredients:
- 1/2 cup organic cocoa powder, unsweetened
- 2 teaspoons monk fruit sweetener syrup
- 2 teaspoons peppermint extract, unsweetened
- 1/2 cup coconut butter, melted
- 1/2 cup coconut oil

Directions:
1. Place coconut oil in a heatproof bowl and microwave for 1 minute or more until oil melts completely, stirring halfway through.
2. Remove bowl from oven and whisk in cocoa powder until smooth.
3. Take 24 muffin cups, line with muffin liner and evenly pour in half of the cocoa mixture in such a way that sides are covered with the mixture.
4. Place muffin cups into the freezer for 15 minutes or until firm.
5. In the meantime, place coconut butter in a bowl and microwave for 1 minute or until butter melts, stirring halfway through.
6. Whisk melted butter well until creamy and then whisk in peppermint extract until smooth.
7. Take out each muffin cup, then spoon in coconut butter mixture and then cover with remaining cocoa mixture.
8. Return muffin cups into the freezer and chill for 15 minutes or more until firm.
9. When ready to serve, take out shells from muffin cups and serve.

Coconut Cookies

Prepping Time: 10 minutes

Cook Time: 0 minutes

Smart Points: 3

Servings: 20

Ingredients:
- 3 cups shredded coconut flakes, unsweetened
- 1/2 cup monk fruit syrup
- 1 cup coconut oil, melted

Directions:
1. Place all the ingredients in a mixing bowl and stir until mixed.

2.   Use wet hands to shape mixture into 20 small cookie balls and place a baking tray, lined with a parchment sheet.

3.   Use a fork to slightly press each cookie and then place baking sheet into the refrigerator until firm.

4.   Serve when ready.

No Bake Cookies

Prepping Time: 10 minutes

Cook Time: 0 minutes

Smart Points: 4

Servings: 9

Ingredients:

- 1 cup shredded coconut, unsweetened
- 1 tablespoon organic cocoa powder, unsweetened
- 2 tablespoons cashew butter
- 4 drops vanilla stevia
- 2/3 cup peanut butter

Directions:

1.   Place cashew butter and peanut butter in a heatproof bowl and stir until smooth.

2.   Then add coconut, cocoa powder, and stevia until well combined.

3.   Take a baking sheet, line it with parchment paper and place coconut mixture on it, each about 2 inches.

4.   Place the baking sheet into the freezer and chill for 15 minutes or until hard.

5.   Serve straightaway.

Mascarpone Cheese Mousse

Prepping Time: 5 minutes

Cook Time: 0 minutes

Smart Points: 4

Servings: 12

Ingredients:

- 1 cup blueberries, organic
- 1 cup strawberries, organic
- 3/4 teaspoon vanilla stevia
- 8 ounces mascarpone cheese, full-fat
- 1 cup whipping cream, full-fat

Directions:

1.   Place cream and cheese in a large bowl and whip using an electric stand mixer until well combined.

2. Spoon the mixture into bowls, top with berries in layers and serve.

White Chocolate Fat Bombs

Prepping Time: 5 minutes
Cook Time: 1 minute
Smart Points: 4
Servings: 8

Ingredients:
- 10 drops vanilla stevia
- 1/4 cup coconut oil
- 1/4 cup cocoa butter, organic

Directions:

1. Place butter and coconut oil in a heatproof bowl and microwave at high heat setting for 1 minute or more until butter melt completely, stirring halfway through.

2. Then whisk in vanilla until well mixed and pour this mixture into molds.

3. Place molds into the freezer or until mixture are harden.

4. When ready to serve, take out a fat bomb from the molds and serve.

Chapter 6: Snacks

Tart Raspberry Crumble Bar

Cook Time: 45 minutes

Smart Points: 3

Servings: 9

Ingredients:

- 1/2 cup whole toasted almonds
- 1 3/4 cups whole wheat flour
- 1/4 teaspoon salt
- 3/4 cup cold, unsalted butter, cut into cubes
- 3 tablespoons cold water, or more if needed
- 1/2 cup granulated sugar
- 18-ounce fresh raspberries

Directions:

1. In a food processor, pulse almonds until copped coarsely. Transfer to a bowl.

2. Add flour and salt into food processor and pulse until a bit combined. Add butter and pulse until you have a coarse batter. Evenly divide batter into two bowls.

3. In first bowl of batter, knead well until it forms a ball. Wrap in cling wrap, flatten a bit and chill for an hour for easy handling.

4. In second bowl of batter, add sugar. In a pinching motion, pinch batter to form clusters of streusel. Set aside.

5. When ready to bake, preheat oven to 375oF and lightly grease an 8x8-inch baking pan with cooking spray.

6. Discard cling wrap and evenly press dough on bottom of pan, up to 1-inch up the sides of the pan, making sure that everything is covered in dough.

7. Evenly spread raspberries. Top with streusel.

8. Pop in the oven and bake until golden brown and berries are bubbly, around 45 minutes.

9. Remove from oven and cool for 20 minutes before slicing into 9 equal bars.

10. Serve and enjoy or store in a lidded container for 10-days in the fridge.

Blueberry Coffee Cake Muffins

Cook Time: 25 minutes

Smart Points: 3

Servings: 16

Ingredients:

- 12 tablespoons (1 1/2 sticks) unsalted butter, at room temperature

- 1 1/2 cups sugar
- 3 extra-large eggs, at room temperature
- 1 1/2 teaspoons pure vanilla extract
- 8 ounces (about 1 cup) sour cream, light
- 1/4 cup skim milk
- 2 1/2 cups all-purpose flour
- 2 teaspoons baking powder
- 1/2 teaspoon baking soda
- 2 half-pints fresh blueberries

Directions:

1. Preheat the oven to 350oF and line muffin tins with muffin liners.
2. Cream butter and sugar until light and fluffy in a large mixing bowl for 5 minutes with a mixer.
3. On low speed, add the eggs 1 at a time, then add the vanilla, sour cream, and milk.
4. Add baking soda and baking powder. Mix for a minute.
5. Add flour and beat until just mixed.
6. With a spatula, fold in blueberries.
7. Evenly add batter on to prepared muffin tins, filling each cup just over the top.
8. Bake for 25 minutes or until muffins are lightly browned on top.
9. Serve and enjoy. Muffins can be store in a tightly lidded container in the fridge for up to a week.

Healthy Banana-Choco Ice Cream

Smart Points: 3

Servings: 4

Cook Time: 0 minutes

Ingredients:

- 3 medium bananas, peeled and frozen
- 3 tbsp Unsweetened Cocoa Powder
- 1/2 tsp peppermint extract

Directions:

1. Place all ingredients in a blender and puree until it resembles a soft serve ice cream.
2. Evenly divide into 4 bowls.
3. Serve and enjoy.

Broccoli Fritters with Cheddar Cheese

Prepping Time: 20 mins

Smart Points: 4

Servings: 4

Ingredients

- 1 cup cheddar cheese, shredded
- 8 ounces broccoli, chopped, steamed and drained
- 2 large eggs, beaten
- 1 tablespoon avocado oil
- 2 tablespoons oat fiber

Directions

1. Mix together broccoli with cheddar cheese, eggs and oat fiber in a bowl.
2. Heat avocado oil over medium heat in a nonstick pan and add the broccoli mixture in small chunks.
3. Cook for about 5 minutes on both sides until browned and dish onto a platter to serve.

Caprese Snack

Prepping Time: 5 mins

Smart Points: 4

Servings: 4

Ingredients

- 8 oz. mozzarella, mini cheese balls
- 8 oz. cherry tomatoes
- 2 tablespoons green pesto
- Salt and black pepper, to taste
- 1 tablespoon garlic powder

Directions

1. Slice the mozzarella balls and tomatoes in half.
2. Stir in the green pesto and season with garlic powder, salt and pepper to serve.

Almond Flour Crackers

Prepping Time: 25 mins

Smart Points: 4

Servings: 6

Ingredients

- 2 tablespoons sunflower seeds
- 1 cup almond flour
- ¾ teaspoon sea salt

- 1 tablespoon whole psyllium husks
- 1 tablespoon coconut oil

Directions

1. Preheat the oven to 3500F and grease a baking sheet lightly.
2. Mix together sunflower seeds, almond flour, sea salt, coconut oil, psyllium husks and 2 tablespoons of water in a bowl.
3. Transfer into a blender and blend until smooth.
4. Form a dough out of this mixture and roll it on the parchment paper until 1/16 inch thick.
5. Slice into 1-inch squares and season with some sea salt.
6. Arrange the squares on the baking sheet and transfer to the oven.
7. Bake for about 15 minutes until edges are crisp and brown.
8. Allow to cool and separate into squares to serve.

Cheesy Radish

Prepping Time: 1 hour

Smart Points: 4

Servings: 5

Ingredients

- 16 oz. Monterey jack cheese, shredded
- 2 cups radish
- ½ cup heavy cream
- 1 teaspoon lemon juice
- Salt and white pepper, to taste

Directions

1. Preheat the oven to 3000F and lightly grease a baking sheet.
2. Heat heavy cream in a small saucepan and season with salt and white pepper.
3. Stir in Monterey jack cheese and lemon juice.
4. Place the radish on the baking sheet and top with the cheese mixture.
5. Bake for about 45 minutes and remove from the oven to serve hot.

Healthy Buckwheat Groats and Seeds Granola

Cook Time: 30 minutes

Smart Points: 1

Servings: 18

Ingredients:

- 1 1/2 cups raw buckwheat groats
- 1 1/2 cups rolled oats

- 1/4 cup chopped pecans
- 1/4 cup chopped cashews
- 1/2 cup unsweetened coconut flakes
- 2 tbsp sunflower seeds
- 4 tbsppepitas
- 3/4 tsp ground cinnamon
- 1/4 cup olive oil
- 1/2 cup maple syrup
- 3 tbsp almond butter
- 3 tbsp coconut sugar
- 1/3 cup dried blueberries

Directions:

1. Preheat oven to 325oF.
2. In a large mixing bowl, mix well groats, oats, pecans, cashews, coconut flakes, sunflower seeds, pepitas, and cinnamon.
3. Place a small nonstick pot on medium fire and heat oil for 2 minutes. Stir in maple syrup and mix well. Add almond butter and coconut sugar. Mix thoroughly until smooth and creamy.
4. Pour sauce into bowl of groats and toss well to coat and mix.
5. Lightly grease a baking sheet with cooking spray.
6. Evenly spread granola on to baking sheet. Pop in the oven and bake for 30 minutes or until a deep golden brown. Halfway through cooking time, toss around granola for even cooking.
7. Remove from oven and toss in dried fruit. Allow to cool completely.
8. Evenly divide into ¼ cups. Store in zip lock bags for up to 3 weeks.

Crispy Baked Zucchini Fries

Prepping Time: 30 mins

Smart Points: 3

Servings: 4

Ingredients
- ¾ cup parmesan cheese, grated
- 2 medium zucchinis, chopped into small sticks
- 1 large egg
- ¼ teaspoon black pepper
- ¼ teaspoon garlic powder

Directions

1. Preheat the oven to 4250F and grease a baking sheet lightly.

2. Whisk egg in one bowl and mix together parmesan cheese, black pepper and garlic powder in another bowl.

3. Dip each zucchini stick in the egg and then dredge in the dry mixture.

4. Transfer to the baking sheet and place in the oven.

5. Bake for about 20 minutes until golden and broil for 3 minutes to serve.

Easy Coconut-Carrot Cake Balls

Cook Time: 0 minutes

Smart Points: 3

Servings: 16

Ingredients:

- 3/4 cup peeled and finely shredded carrot
- 1 cup packed pitted medjool dates
- 1 ¾ cups raw walnuts
- 3/4 tsp ground cinnamon
- 1/2 tsp ground ginger
- 1 pinch ground nutmeg
- 2 tsp vanilla extract
- 5 tbsp almond flour
- 1/4 cup raisins
- ¼ cup desiccated coconut flakes

Directions:

1. In food processor, process dates until it clumps. Transfer to a bowl.

2. In same food processor, process walnuts, cinnamon, ginger, and nutmeg. Process until it resembles a fine meal.

3. Add the processed dates, extract, almond flour, and shredded carrots. Pulse until you form a loose dough but not mushy. Do not over-pulse. Transfer to a bowl.

4. Pulse desiccated coconut into tinier flakes and transfer to a small plate.

5. Divide the carrot batter into 4 and then divide each part into 4 to make a total of 16 equal sized balls.

6. Roll the balls in the coconut flakes, place in a lidded contained, and refrigerate for 2 hours before enjoying.

7. Can be stored in the fridge for a week and up to a month in the freezer.

Pumpkin Walnut Cookie

Cook Time: 30 minutes

Smart Points: 2

Servings: 24

Ingredients:

- 1 tbsp baking powder
- ½ tsp salt
- 1½ tsp pumpkin pie spice mix
- 1¼ cups whole wheat flour
- 1½ cups flour
- ½ cup vegetable oil
- 2 eggs
- 1 cup brown sugar
- 3 packets Stevia
- 1 ¾ cups pumpkin, cooked and pureed (15 oz. can)
- 1 cup walnuts or hazelnuts, chopped
- 1 cup raisin

Directions:

1. Grease a cookie sheet with cooking spray and preheat oven to 400oF.
2. In a medium bowl mix baking powder, salt, pumpkin pie spice mix, whole wheat flour, and flour.
3. In a large bowl beat eggs and oil thoroughly.
4. Add in brown sugar and stevia beat for at least 3 minutes.
5. Mix in pumpkin puree and beat well.
6. Slowly add the dry ingredients beating well after each addition.
7. Fold in nuts and raisins.
8. Using a 1 tbsp measuring spoon, get two saltspoonfuls of the dough and place on cookie sheet at least an inch apart. With the bottom of a spoon, flatten cookie.
9. Pop into the oven and bake until golden brown, around 10 minutes.
10. Once done, remove from oven, serve and enjoy or store in tightly lidded containers for up to a week.

Spicy Tuna Rolls

Prepping Time: 15 mins

Smart Points: 3

Servings: 2

Ingredients:

- 1 pouch StarKist Selects E.V.O.O. Wild Caught Yellowfin Tuna
- 1 medium cucumber, thinly sliced lengthwise
- 1 teaspoon hot sauce
- 2 slices avocado, diced
- Cayenne, salt and black pepper

Directions:

1. Mix together tuna with hot sauce, cayenne, salt and black pepper in a bowl until combined.
2. Put the tuna mixture on the cucumber slices and top with avocado.
3. Roll up the cucumber and secure with 2 toothpicks to serve.

Cheesy Low Carb Creamed Spinach

Prepping Time: 25 mins

Smart Points: 4

Servings: 8

Ingredients:
*   2 (10 ozpackages frozen chopped spinach, thawed)
*   3 tablespoons butter
*   6 ounces cream cheese
*   Onion powder, salt and black pepper
*   ½ cup parmesan cheese, grated

Directions:
1. Mix together 2 tablespoons of butter with cream cheese, parmesan cheese, salt and black pepper in a bowl.
2. Heat the rest of the butter on medium heat in a small pan and add onion powder.
3. Sauté for about 1 minute and add spinach.
4. Cover and cook on low heat for about 5 minutes.
5. Stir in the cheese mixture and cook for about 3 minutes.
6. Dish into a bowl and serve hot.

Lemon Glazed Blueberry Scones

Cook Time: 20 minutes

Smart Points: 3

Servings: 8

Ingredients:
*   1/2 cup freshly squeezed lemon juice
*   2 cups confectioners' sugar, sifted
*   1 tablespoon unsalted butter
*   2 cups all-purpose flour
*   1 tablespoon baking powder
*   2 tablespoons sugar
*   5 tablespoons unsalted butter, cold, cut in chunks
*   1 cup fresh blueberries
*   1 cup heavy cream, plus more for brushing the scones

Directions:

1. Make the lemon glaze by mixing lemon juice, confectioner's sugar, and butter. Microwave for 30 seconds and mix well until smooth and creamy. Set aside.

2. Preheat the oven to 400oF.

3. Sift together the flour, baking powder, and sugar. Using 2 forks or a pastry blender, cut in the butter to coat the pieces with the flour. The mixture should look like coarse crumbs. Fold the blueberries into the batter.

4. Make a well in the center and pour in the heavy cream. Fold everything together just to incorporate; do not overwork the dough.

5. Evenly divide dough into 8. Form each dough into triangles.

6. Place the scones on an ungreased cookie sheet and brush the tops with a little heavy cream. Bake for 15 to 20 minutes until beautifully browned.

7. Let the scones cool a bit before you apply the glaze.

8. Serve and enjoy

Healthy Blueberry & Banana Muffins

Cook Time: 25 minutes

Smart Points: 3

Servings: 12

Ingredients:

- 3/4 cup mashed ripe banana
- 3/4 cup + 2 tablespoons unsweetened almond milk
- 1 teaspoon apple cider vinegar
- 1/4 cup pure maple syrup
- 1 teaspoon pure vanilla extract
- 1/4 cup coconut oil, melted
- 1/2 teaspoon baking soda
- 2 teaspoons baking powder
- 4 tablespoons coconut sugar
- 1 1/2 teaspoons cinnamon
- 2 cups white spelt flour
- 1 1/4 cups frozen or fresh blueberries
- 1/2 cup walnut halves, chopped

Directions:

1. Preheat oven to 350oF.

2. In a large mixing bowl, whisk well all wet ingredients.

3. Slowly add in dry ingredients, mixing well every after each addition.

4. Line 12 muffin tins with cupcake liners and evenly fill liners with batter.

5. Bake for 25 minutes.

6. Serve and enjoy.

Jicama Fries

Prepping Time: 20 mins

Smart Points: 3

Servings: 2

Ingredients:

- 2 tablespoons avocado oil
- 1 Jicama, cut into fries
- 1 tablespoon garlic powder
- ½ cup parmesan cheese, grated
- Salt and black pepper, to taste

Directions:

1. Preheat the Air fryer to 4000F and grease the fryer basket.
2. Boil jicama fries for about 10 minutes and drain well.
3. Mix jicama fries with garlic powder, salt and black pepper in a bowl.
4. Place in the fryer basket and cook for about 10 minutes.
5. Dish onto a platter and serve warm.

Choco-Chip Cookies with Walnuts and Oatmeal

Cook Time: 16 minutes

Smart Points: 2

Servings: 24

Ingredients:

- ½ tsp salt
- ½ tsp baking soda
- 1 tsp ground cinnamon
- ½ cup whole wheat pastry flour
- ½ cup all-purpose flour
- 2 cups rolled oats (not quick cooking)
- 4 tbsp cold unsalted butter, cut into pieces
- ½ cup tahini
- 2/3 cup packed light brown sugar
- 6 packets Stevia
- 1 tbsp vanilla extract
- 1 large egg white
- 1 large egg
- ½ cup chopped walnuts

- 1 cup semisweet Choco chip

Directions:

1. Position two racks in the middle of the oven, leaving at least a 3-inch space in between them. Preheat oven to 350oF and grease baking sheets with cooking spray.

2. In medium bowl, whisk together salt, baking soda, cinnamon, whole wheat flour, all-purpose flour and oats.

3. In a large bowl, with a mixer beat butter and tahini until well combined.

4. Add brown sugar and Stevia, mixing continuously until creamy.

5. Mix in vanilla, egg white and egg and beat for a minute.

6. Cup by cup mix in the dry ingredients until well incorporated.

7. Fold in walnuts and Choco chips.

8. Get two tablespoonfuls of the batter and roll with your moistened hands into a ball.

9. Evenly place balls into prepped baking sheets at least an inch apart.

10. Pop in the oven and bake for 16 minutes. Ten minutes into baking time, switch pans from top to bottom and bottom to top. Continue baking for 6 more minutes.

11. Remove from oven, cool on a wire rack. Allow pans to cool completely before adding the next batch of cookies to be baked.

12. Cookies can be stored for up to 10 days in a tightly sealed container or longer in the fridge.

Low Carb Onion Rings

Prepping Time: 30 mins

Smart Points: 3

Servings: 6

Ingredients:

- 2 medium white onions, sliced into ½ inch thick rings
- ½ cup coconut flour
- 4 large eggs
- 4 oz pork rinds
- 1 cup parmesan cheese, grated

Directions:

1. Preheat an Air fryer to 3900F and grease a fryer basket.

2. Put coconut flour in one bowl, eggs in the second bowl and pork rinds and parmesan cheese in the third bowl.

3. Coat the onion rings through the three bowls one by one and repeat.

4. Place the coated onion rings in the fryer basket and cook for about 15 minutes.

5. Dish out to a platter and serve with your favorite low carb sauce.

Tart Raspberry Crumble Bar

Cook Time: 45 minutes

Smart Points: 3

Servings: 9

Ingredients:

- 1/2 cup whole toasted almonds
- 1 3/4 cups whole wheat flour
- 1/4 teaspoon salt
- 3/4 cup cold, unsalted butter, cut into cubes
- 3 tablespoons cold water, or more if needed
- 1/2 cup granulated sugar
- 18-ounce fresh raspberries

Directions:

1. In a food processor, pulse almonds until copped coarsely. Transfer to a bowl.
2. Add flour and salt into food processor and pulse until a bit combined. Add butter and pulse until you have a coarse batter. Evenly divide batter into two bowls.
3. In first bowl of batter, knead well until it forms a ball. Wrap in cling wrap, flatten a bit and chill for an hour for easy handling.
4. In second bowl of batter, add sugar. In a pinching motion, pinch batter to form clusters of streusels. Set aside.
5. When ready to bake, preheat oven to 375oF and lightly grease an 8x8-inch baking pan with cooking spray.
6. Discard cling wrap and evenly press dough on bottom of pan, up to 1-inch up the sides of the pan, making sure that everything is covered in dough.
7. Evenly spread raspberries. Top with streusel.

Healthy Chocolate Mousse

Cook Time: 0 minutes; Smart Points: 2; Servings: 4

Ingredients:

- 1 large, ripe avocado
- 1/4 cup sweetened almond milk
- 1 tbsp coconut oil
- 1/4 cup cocoa or cacao powder
- 1 tsp vanilla extract

Directions:

1. In food processor, process all ingredients until smooth and creamy.
2. Transfer to a lidded container and chill for at least 4 hours.
3. Serve and enjoy.

Conclusion

I hope this book could provide you with plenty of ideas for recipes that won't just flavor good, they shall carry out the body good as well. The next thing is to stop reading already and to begin cooking up slow cooker recipes you will be capable to feel great about eating.

Consider the recipes outlined above as a starter information and build on them as you move, keeping in mind stage requirements as needed and you will be looking and feeling much better than you ever thought feasible earlier than you could ever imagine.

Thank you and good luck!